Dewdrops of Infinity

Psychedelics, Psychic Abilities, UFOs, and
THE PUHARICH PROJECT

COLOR EDITION   Sean McNamara

Also by the author

Renegade Mystic

The Pursuit of Spiritual Freedom Through Consciousness Exploration

Second Edition

SEAN MCNAMARA

Also by the author

Online Courses from Sean McNamara

at

www.LifeTending.net

- Executive System Weight Loss Program

- Vagus Nerve Stimulation for Meditation and Wellness

- Guided Meditation Journeys

- And more!

To Carol C.,
Small conversations with you
make big things happen.
Thank you for your magic.

BLUE THUMB

How to Grow Psilocybin Mushrooms at Home

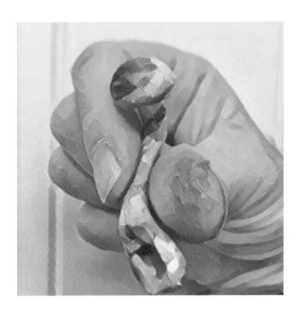

The Experiential Step-by-Step,
Picture-by-Picture Guide

COLOR EDITION

Sean McNamara

First Edition

Published by
Mind Possible

www.MindPossible.com

www.LifeTending.net

ISBN: 978-1-7352930-9-7 (Color Edition)

TABLE OF CONTENTS

PART ONE:

INTRODUCTION

Pictures, Pictures, Pictures

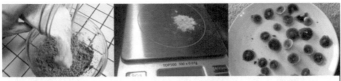

We all learn better through *experience*.

Pictures convey experience *better* than words alone.

This guide includes over 300 pictures to help you feel *comfortable* learning and *confident* growing psilocybin mushrooms on your own.

Part One: Introduction

Introducing the Moniker
Blue Thumb

One morning, after carefully cleaning the stems from a fresh crop of psilocybin mushrooms, I noticed my thumb was stained blue. Psilocybin mushrooms typically bruise blue within a minute or two of being handled. It's how many people identify them in the wild.

Also, the moniker *green thumb* describes a person with a talent for growing plants. So, this is just a cute twist on the name, given that mushrooms are not plants, they are fungi.

I recently learned that people who focus on the conservation and intelligent use of water are also called *blue thumbs*. I believe both types of blue thumbs have a keen understanding of our natural environment and the need for its conservation.

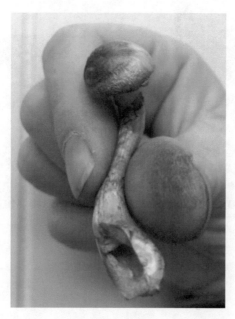

Blue Thumb   Sean McNamara

My Motivation for Writing Blue Thumb

At one point in my life, I participated in a year-long study to investigate whether psilocybin, Amanita muscaria, LSD, and DMT would improve psychic abilities such as clairvoyance, precognition, and telepathy.[1]

During the period dedicated to microdosing psilocybin, I unexpectedly experienced a drastic reduction of my anxiety. It was significant. My wife noticed the shift almost as quickly as I did because of the sudden decrease of my usual over-reactivity and rumination when confronting life's daily frustrations.

I also wondered if I'd been living most of my life in a clinically depressed state and didn't even know it. It felt as if a dark cloud I'd never noticed before suddenly lifted. I experienced a considerable shift in my default level of happiness, or rather, lack of happiness.

Taking psilocybin on the predetermined mornings was easy and quick. It took one minute to measure the pinch of blue-gray powder on my electronic kitchen scale then slide it into my bowl of oatmeal.

I was on a strict schedule, and I didn't take it every day. And the point wasn't to hallucinate or enter an altered state of consciousness. In fact, I wasn't meant to feel *anything*.

A "micro" dose is a *sub-perceptual* dose, meaning that a person should not feel anything at all from such a

---

[1] You can read about the study, its results, and the mysterious phenomena that occurred during and in between the tests that year in my book "Dewdrops of Infinity: Psychedelics, Psychic Abilities, UFOs, and the Puharich Project."

Part One: Introduction

tiny portion. What I realized from my own direct experience was that psilocybin was medicine for my mind, and a highly effective, natural one at that. And it was one I could learn to grow at home.

I live in Denver, Colorado, where psilocybin mushrooms achieved *decriminalized* status in 2019. This means that although it is still illegal to possess, buy, or sell psilocybin, arresting people for simple possession is now the lowest priority for law enforcement.

This means that police can focus more on tasks like arresting lethal drivers under the influence of *legal* alcohol, arresting people for shooting other people with *legal* handguns and *legal* automated weapons…I'm sure you catch my drift.

Meanwhile, healthcare workers spend time treating major portions of the population for cardiovascular diseases due to smoking *legal*, chemically enhanced tobacco.

For medical patients struggling with physical pain, some (not all) doctors prescribe *legal* opioids to excess, resulting in our national opioid crisis.

Therapists and other mental health care workers support people struggling with their addiction to *legal* online and casino gambling, an addiction which most insurance companies still won't cover the treatment of. They're also treating people addicted to *legal* pornography.

Incidentally, "process" addictions like gambling and pornography stimulate the brain similarly to cocaine, which is exactly why they're so addictive. Addiction is not a moral issue. It's a chemical one.

> # Save $2.00
> # when you buy two!
>
> **SURGEON GENERAL'S WARNING:**
>
> Smoking Causes Lung Cancer,
> Heart Disease, Emphysema,
> And May Complicate Pregnancy.
>
> **... but it's totally legal.**

Depression often causes or accompanies addiction, whether the addiction is to a *substance* like alcohol, or to a *process* like gambling or binge-watching television every night after work.

As an aside, I'm not saying the solution is to make these substances or activities illegal. These are symptoms. They are coping behaviors. They are not the root cause. I only highlight them to point out society's crippling hypocrisy.

I think of my uncle who struggled with depression and other mental conditions for decades. The psychiatrists did their best to offer a combination of pharmaceutical drugs to support him. But the drugs didn't work, and one terrible, heartbreaking day, my uncle ended his suffering by committing suicide by handgun.

I wonder if psilocybin could have helped my uncle's mind similarly to the way it helped mine.

Part One: Introduction

I wonder if psilocybin could have helped the any of the more than 114,000 veterans who have committed suicide since 2001.[2]

According to StopSoldierSuicide.org, "there has been an 86% increase in suicide rate among 18-to-34-year-old male veterans" since 2006. So young.

Ironically, suicide is listed as a potential side effect, especially in young people (18-24) who take SSRI antidepressant medications.

According to the website Drugwatch.com, "In 2004, the U.S. Food and Drug Administration (FDA) issued a black box warning – the agency's strictest warning – for all selective serotonin reuptake inhibitors (SSRI) antidepressants regarding their association with suicidal thoughts and behaviors."[3]

I should mention the fact that doctors, people who presumably have the very best access to medicine, suffer the highest suicide rate of any profession, with one doctor committing suicide every single day, on average.[4]

Recently, medical researchers have begun clinical trials to determine the possible medical benefits of psilocybin. But the process is slow, and while a very small number of fortunate study participants get to experience the mushroom's benefits, hundreds of thousands of people are forced to wait.

---

[2] StopSoldierSuicide.org/vet-stats

[3] DrugWatch.com/ssri/suicide/

[4] WebMD.com/mental-health/news/20180508/doctors-suicide-rate-highest-of-any-profession

They will probably wait for years, if not decades, depending on the sometimes-terrifying trajectory of this country's political and social values.

Do you wonder why psilocybin is still a DEA Schedule 1 drug, defined as having "no currently accepted medical use and a high potential for abuse"[5] even though there is sufficient, recent, scientific evidence that the DEA classification is <u>flat out wrong</u>, in my opinion?

Reflect on the politicians and "moral" or religious leaders who are either innocently unaware of the newest data, or who choose to ignore it in support of their personal and organizational agendas.

Their professional survival depends on *not* rocking the boat, even if it's for the betterment of others.

By the way, according to the article *Shedding Light on Classic Psychedelics and Self-Harm* by Grossman and Hendricks found on Psychiatrist.com, a recent study "which analyzed suicidality data from 7 classic psychedelic therapy trials ... found acute and sustained **decreases** on all relevant measures."[6]

And from Drugpolicy.org, "Psilocybin is not considered to be addictive, nor does it cause compulsive use."[7]

This is all a long way of saying **my motivation to write this guide is to help people.**

---

[5] DEA.gov/drug-information/drug-scheduling

[6] Psychiatrist.com/jcp/depression/suicide/shedding-light-classic-psychedelics-self-harm/

[7] DrugPolicy.org/drug-facts/are-psilocybin-mushrooms-addictive

And the decriminalization of psilocybin in places[8] like Denver CO, Oakland and Santa Cruz CA, Washington, D.C., Somerville, Cambridge, and Northampton MA, and Seattle WA makes it possible for me to write Blue Thumb in good conscience.

I will not break the law by selling or distributing mushrooms. But I can write books. We still have the freedom of speech in the United States, at least to some degree.

And, you know the old saying, "If you give someone a fish, they eat for a day. But if you teach them how to grow psilocybin mushrooms, they'll have access to potentially good medicine for a lifetime."

Whether or not you live in a decriminalized area, it is your responsibility to be aware of the law. This book does not offer legal advice. It also does not offer medical advice. It does not offer ethical advice. It is a book about how to grow fungi and grow it well.

Therefore, I recommend you consult with your lawyer, your doctor, your therapist, and your religious or *spiritual* authority (hopefully that person is *you*) before growing and consuming your own psilocybin mushrooms.

If you decide to use this book, **please be a responsible user.** Pay special attention in Part Nine, *Harm Reduction*.

Work <u>with </u>the law, not against it. Help maintain psilocybin's increasingly positive light in the media by not doing anything stupid.

And vote.

8

https://en.wikipedia.org/wiki/Psilocybin_decriminalization_in_the_United_States

As a mature, responsible, and politically active adult, you can support society's quest for health, happiness, safety, and common sense.

Be good.

How to Best Approach These Instructions

This guide will teach you two convenient methods for growing at home. But as you see in the table of contents, it will also teach you what to do with your crop after you've harvested it.

Even more, it will teach you how to continue nature's cycle with various methods for cultivating your own spores and mycelium for long-term, budget-friendly continuity.

To help you follow the detailed instructions in Part 3 and Part 4, I've inserted a line in front of the specific action steps so you can check them off with a pencil as you go through your process. This will prevent you accidentally skipping steps. For example:

____ Pour the brown rice flour into the vermiculite-water mix.

As much as possible, pictures will appear immediately after their pertinent instructions. When that is not possible, the instructions will include the picture number and its page number for easy reference. In a few cases, several instructions refer to the same picture.

I recommend you slowly <u>read through the whole guide from beginning to end</u> before deciding which method you want to use, before purchasing supplies.

You'll notice my goal is to be as succinct as possible and let the pictures work as hard as the words. Definitions will come as needed, if not before. If any instruction is unclear to you, take a step back and consider the goal at hand, then use common sense.

PART TWO:

THE ESSENTIALS

Environmental Conditions at Home

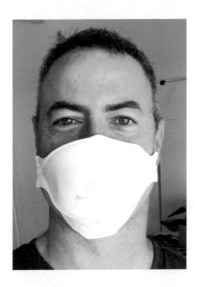

Mushroom growers face four environmental challenges. These are **mold** and **humidity** or its opposite, **dryness**, and **temperature**.

MOLD

Mold is everywhere, on your skin, floating through the air, and living on any surface it lands on. Like other germs, it's invisible. That is, until it grows in perfect conditions necessary for it to proliferate until you can see it or smell it. The problem with mold is that it's nourished by the same two things mushrooms depend on most, nutrition and moisture. You can consider your mushrooms, at any stage, to be in direct competition with mold.

Even the early stages of growing take time and effort. It can feel disappointing to lose a crop to mold whether you inoculated your *substrate* (the nutrient-rich material you introduce mycelium to) a few days ago, or you've made it two months down the line, waiting for your *pins* (think of them as baby mushrooms) to become mature fruits, the mushrooms.

Tossing your hard work into the garbage because of a mold infestation is downright frustrating. But it's preventable.

If you have standing water anywhere in your home, that means you probably have a greater-than-normal amount of mold floating through the air. Do you regularly have bowls and plates piled up in the sink for days? Is any plumbing slowly leaking behind your walls?

Has it been a while since you've sanitized your bathroom, shower, or other wet areas? How often do you vacuum or sweep the floors and wipe down your tables, bookcases, and other flat areas?

Now's the time to clean your home from top to bottom. Cleaning everything up the morning of your first *grow* (I'll sometimes use "grow" as a noun moving forward) might not be a good idea. It's possible you'll kick a lot of remaining mold spores into the air, and it could be a very long time before they settle down onto flat surfaces again. Doing a thorough cleaning a day or two before is better.

Also, your body and clothing are potential mold carriers. Your skin has an excellent immune system, so everything stays in balance. But it serves as a mold transporter. Anytime you do a task where you can accidentally transport mold onto your equipment, substrate, spores, mycelium, etc., you should be clean.

To be clean, take a shower before working on your grow, especially scrubbing old skin cells from your

Part Two: The Essentials

forearms, hands, and face. Then, put on freshly laundered clothing.

Since your breath can transport a variety of germs, wear a facemask.

As for your hands, wear nitrile or similar gloves and wipe them down with isopropyl alcohol using a cotton ball or clean towel. If you don't like the idea of dumping even more synthetic waste into the environment, then give your hands an extra wash with soap right before you start work.

Now that you're informed, mold isn't the real enemy, laziness is.

HUMIDITY AND DRYNESS

One of earliest stages of mushroom farming is growing mycelium. After *inoculating* (introducing) a substrate with *spores* (microscopic reproductive cells), mycelium will begin to grow. *Mycelium* is the main fungal tissue. Mushrooms grow out from it much like flowers or fruits (which contain seeds) grow from plants.

The flower isn't the plant. It's a reproductive extension of the plant. Similarly, mushrooms aren't the main fungal tissue, but rather a reproductive extension of it. We could call mushrooms the *fruit* of the mycelium. Later, you'll learn about *fruiting conditions* in mushroom cultivation.

Both mycelium and its fruit, the mushrooms, depend on water. Mushrooms are around 90% water. This means the substrate they grow from needs to contain enough water to produce them.

This also means the surrounding air needs to be humid enough to prevent the substrate or mushrooms from drying out. Dry mushrooms don't grow.

Controlling moisture during *incubation,* the time when mycelium grows and spreads through the substrate, is relatively simple. But controlling the humidity in your home and in the *monotub* (the container where you'll introduce fruiting conditions), can be tricky.

If you live at an altitude near sea-level and near a coastline, or in a tropical region, achieving high humidity won't be difficult for you.

But if, like me, you live in Denver, Colorado, also known as the "mile-high city" for its altitude, keeping the air humid is a non-stop challenge.

Many online discussion forums include pictures of complicated grow-room setups with humidifiers, hoses, and fans. But none of these are necessary.

I have successfully grown mushrooms by staying watchful of the condensation inside the monotub. When the walls are dry, I simply open the tub and spray them with tap water. Ideally, this only needs to happen twice or three times each day.

Recently, our air conditioner broke down and daytime temperatures inside our home were consistently above 84°F (28.9°C). The heat only hastened the drying out of my monotubs. The solution was a simple misting humidifier I bought online for around $40 (Pic 1, next page).

I set it a couple of feet away from my *tubs* (short for monotubs), aiming the nozzle so the mist was directed toward some of the holes (Pic 2). The little humidifier worked perfectly. I still needed to spray the tub walls a couple times each day, though.

If you live in an extremely humid environment, simply take care *not* to overspray your tubs.

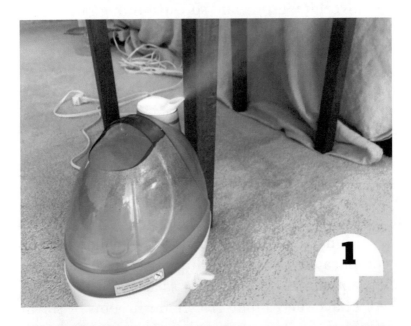

TEMPERATURE

The ambient room temperature for any stage of growth should stay between 70°F (21°C) and 75°F (24°C). However, I've successfully grown mycelium in the high 60's°F, and fruited mushrooms in the mid 80's without any mold contamination. These temperatures were not my choice, but rather because of heating and air conditioning problems in my condominium.

Keep one thing in mind regarding temperatures. The colder it is, the slower everything grows. And the hotter it is, the greater the chance for mold to take over.

Obtaining Spores

As you read earlier, spores are reproductive cells, the starting point for mycelial life. Without spores, you can't grow mushrooms.

Many people assume that you can't purchase spores for psilocybin mushrooms because psilocybin is still illegal in many parts of the world. But this isn't true.

Spores are **legal** to buy in many places because **spores do NOT contain psilocybin**. Psilocybin becomes present sometime after the spores *germinate*, the process of becoming mycelium.

A quick online search using the term "psilocybin spore syringe" will present you with many retailers who can ship directly to you. They sell their spores under the premise that you'll use the spores for "microscopy purposes only." So, you can legally stare at the spores through a *microscope*, but no growing allowed.

Therefore, they usually state clearly on their websites that you may not ask their advice on growing the psilocybin-containing mycelium and mushrooms.

Retailers offer a variety of psilocybin spore strains. "Golden Teacher" is always recommended for beginners, although most strains behave similarly under the same growing conditions. You'll see popular strains such as "Amazonian," "Ecuadorian," "Albino," and "Penis Envy," in most online shops. And yes, Penis Envy mushrooms look exactly how you would imagine.

To begin your first grow, you only need a single spore syringe. It will contain 10 cc's of spore-containing water. Unlike other types of mushroom spores, **psilocybin spores appear black or deep violet.**

You can see a closeup of a psilocybin spore syringe in Pic 3 on the next page.

Don't worry about your delivery lingering too long in your mailbox. Spores are dormant and can survive for long periods in the syringe if conditions aren't extreme. You can store your syringe in a cupboard or your refrigerator for months.

And if you follow all the directions in this guide, this will be the only syringe you ever have to buy again.

Voice of Experience: Once, I received a syringe that contained clear liquid. I couldn't see any spore clumps. A single spore is invisible to the naked eye, so what you see in Pic 3 are clumps of spores. I checked the online forums and saw a few threads claiming that clear syringes are completely fine and still produce mycelium.

Trusting them, I used the syringe on eight jars of substrate. Normally it takes a week or so for the very first wispy strands of mycelium to become visible in a jar. These jars, however, took almost a month before anything appeared. I almost threw them out!

And then it took three times the normal amount of time for them to be completely colonized with mycelium.

So, if you receive a syringe that looks completely clear, it's up to you to use it anyway, or look up your retailer's return/exchange policy. I'm always very happy when I received a nice, dark syringe.

I sacrificed a full syringe (Pic 4) to show you how the fluid appears coming out. When injecting it into a jar, it's difficult to see the fluid through the glass since it's immediately absorbed into the substrate.

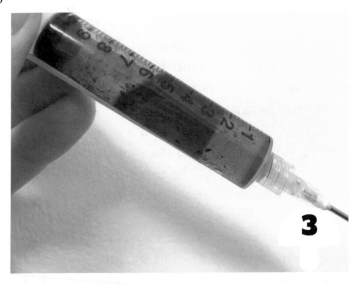

Note: Some retailers sell syringes filled with "liquid culture," meaning they're filled with mycelium instead of spores, saving time during the colonization stage by skipping the stage of waiting for spores to become mycelium. Mycelium is naturally clear or cloudy-white, but some sellers stain the mycelium with charcoal for visibility.

The Indispensable Pressure Cooker

Pressure cookers kill mold and bacteria through the combination of heat and pressure. It's extremely thorough, which is why most of the food sold in jars inside your grocery store have been through this kind of *sterilization* process. Sterilization kills everything.

You might come across techniques elsewhere involving *pasteurization*. This involves heating over several hours with boiled water which eventually cools down. But no pressure is used. There are also chemically based methods of pasteurization, but these are outside the scope of this book.

When you want to make sure every unwanted germ is dead, dead, dead, sterilize with a pressure cooker. I use a 23-quart Presto Pressure Canner and Cooker (Pic 5, next page).

You might borrow one (even if it's smaller) from a friend for your first time to determine the best size for you. The main determinant is how much substrate you want to sterilize at the same time.

Depending on which methods in this guide you use, you'll use your pressure cooker to sterilize:

- substrate
- liquid culture media
- agar plate media
- blades, spoons
- used spore syringes
- glass marbles

Caution: Read your cooker's instruction manual carefully. A misused cooker has the potential to quickly become a deadly bomb.

The lid has an emergency pressure-relief valve and another release valve beneath the "rocker." But you can accidentally block them by putting expandable materials inside, such as plastic bags, which swell up and seal the valves from inside the lid.

None of the methods in this guide involve the use of plastic bags. Instead, you'll take full advantage of your canning jars and discover how versatile they are.

Choosing and Preparing Your Jars

You will use your jars for sterilizing substrate in the pressure cooker. This means you must purchase *canning jars*, specifically designed for use with a pressure cooker. Not only can they tolerate the heat and pressure, but their lids are specifically designed to provide a perfect seal.

Be careful when shopping for jars, as some stores sell jars that resemble canning jars, but it's only for appearance.

The two major brands in the United States are Ball and Pur. Your local home and garden store, or hardware store probably carries canning supplies.

GO WIDE (MOUTH)

In Pic 6 (next page), you see three jars. The two jars on the right are "wide mouth" jars, which are the type you need for preparing substrate. The reason depends on which method you're using.

In Method 1, you'll inoculate the jars with spores, which will grow into mycelium, colonizing the entire jar, forming a *cake*. When colonization is complete, you'll *birth the cake* from the jar. This is easy to do with a wide mouth jar. But with a mason jar (on the left side of the picture) which has a tapered neck, you won't be able to slide the cake out without destroying it.

Wide mouth jars are required. You can use either 8 oz. jars or 16 oz. jars. Your decision on which size to use will depend on the size of your monotub. If you're using an 18-liter tub, then the 8 oz. jars may be more suitable. For a 50-liter tub, the 16 oz. jars are better.

Both sizes of jar are sold in 12-packs and come with lids.

MASON JARS FOR LIQUID CULTURE

Mason jars such as the one on the left side in Pic 6 are useful if you decide to make your own liquid culture, or if you want to sterilize a used spore syringe. These techniques are discussed later in this guide. Those stages are a few months from the start of a new grow, so there's no need to purchase a mason jar at the beginning.

Voice of Experience: I use both major brands of jars. But you may prefer one style over the other because of how easy it is to see through the glass. During the colonization process, when the mycelium spreads through the substrate, it's important to be on the lookout for mold.

A glass jar with intricate designs on it can make spotting mold more difficult. Can you see the mold in Pic 7?

Lid Modification

The jar lids will need two holes. Each hole has a unique purpose.

The first hole, located close to the lid's edge, allows the syringe needle to enter the jar after sterilization to inoculate the substrate with spores.

It must be covered by a *self-healing injection port*. *Self-healing* means when the needle is withdrawn, the puncture automatically closes, preventing outside contaminants from penetrating the jar. Self-healing injection ports come in black or white on adhesive strips, as in Pic 8.

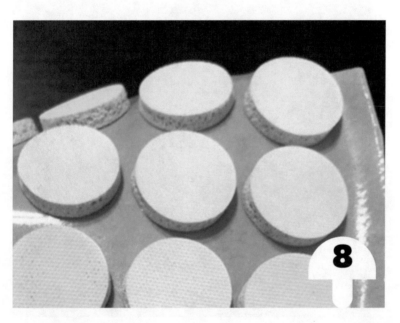

An alternative to using pre-made injection ports is to use a tube of hi-temp RTV silicone sealant, which comes in a metal tube.

Squeeze a small amount over the hole, then let it sit at least 24 hours for it to cure. Pic 9 shows an example. It's the red dab. Make sure it expands *through* the hole when applying it, so that it doesn't easily peel off the lid during inoculation when pulling the syringe out. The other hole is covered by micropore tape.

The second hole, nearer to the center of the lid, is covered by micropore tape. This tape allows for *gas exchange* (as opposed to *fresh air exchange*). The holes in the micropore tape allow air molecules to pass through, due to temperature or pressure shifts while sterilizing or during colonization.

The holes are small enough to prevent mold and other invaders from entering. Gas exchange is sometimes confused with the term *fresh air exchange.*

As you'll see later in the guide, you will create a monotub, including drilling holes into the sides and lid to freely allow air to enter and leave the tub. That is fresh air exchange. The holes are filled with polyester wadding, also known as polyfill, which is intended to keep insects out and help retain humidity.

Part Two: The Essentials

To find micropore tape online, you can search using the name of the manufacturer "3M," using a phrase such as "3M micropore tape." Micropore can come in rolls, or as small disks as seen below in Pic 10. Other companies also sell micropore tape.

You can also do an online search with the phrase "filter disk mushroom." Look at the search results' pictures carefully and compare them to Pic 10 to make sure you're getting the correct size. The size of the filter holes which gasses pass through should be 0.3 µm (µm is spoken as "micron" or "micrometer").

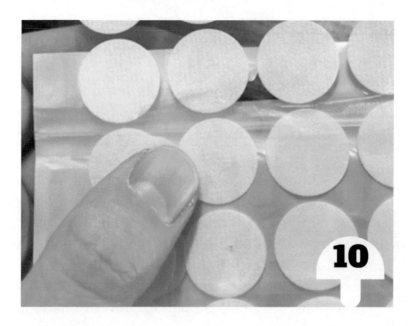

MAKING THE LID HOLES

You can use a rubber mallet or a hammer, and a very thick nail, spike, or awl, as in Pics 11 and 12, below.

Voice of Experience: Notice the one of the holes is centered over the labeling line near the edge in Pics 13 and 14. This makes it easier to find the hole when piercing the injection port with the syringe's needle.

A Very Clean Workspace

Earlier, in the chapter *Environmental Conditions at Home*, you learned about the importance of maintaining good cleanliness throughout your home to reduce the amount of mold and other contaminants floating in the air.

But this isn't enough to prevent contamination while you're inoculating your jars, combining substrates, pouring or transferring agar, etc. You must create an enclosed environment which further prevents contamination.

Two options are presented here, a Still Air Box and a homemade Flow Hood. **You only need one of them.** The main difference between them is cost and complexity. As for creating a sterile environment, it's difficult to say how much better one is than the other.

If cost is not a limitation for you, you might consider purchasing a real, laboratory-grade laminar flow hood, with prices starting near $500. These will offer the highest level of protection against air-borne contaminants.

Making a Still Air Box

A still air box is an inverted clear plastic storage container with two holes in it for your arms to pass through. When selecting your storage container, remember that it should be wide enough to hold multiple jars or other objects. It should also be tall enough to allow you to hold a syringe above a jar. Remember that a spore syringe arrives with the plunger extended, doubling the length of the syringe.

Make sure the sides and the bottom of the container are clear enough for you to see through, as in Pic 15. Many containers have bottoms with lines or indentations in them, making it difficult to see through.

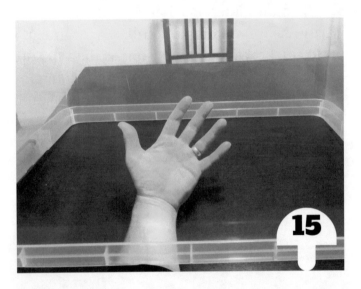

When it's time to choose where to cut the holes, remember to flip the container upside-down (Pic 16), since that's how you'll be using it.

Draw two circles, shoulder-width apart (Pic 17)

Blue Thumb   Sean McNamara

Voice of Experience: When deciding how large to make the holes, grasp one of the jars you'll use for sterilizing your substrate by its base, and notice how wide your grip is. The holes must be large enough to let you pass jars into the box since you don't want to lift it up to put things inside (and allow dirty air to enter).

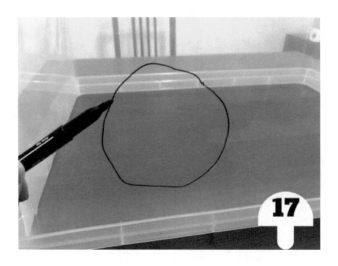

Pics 18, 19, and 20 explain the rest of the process. When drilling, **push the drill bit through slowly**, otherwise you may crack the plastic.

Caution: Wear eye protection, flying shards are sharp!

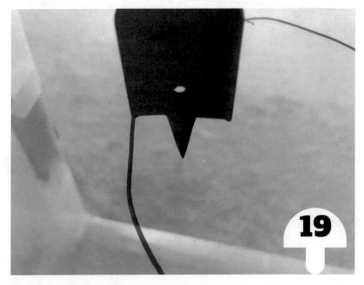

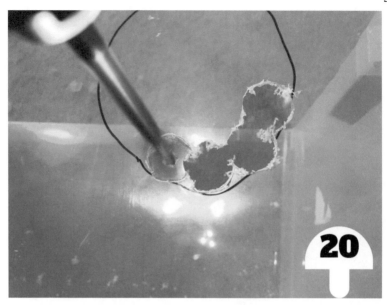

Pic 21 shows me cleaning inside of the box. I recommend a ratio of 9 parts water to 1 part liquid bleach. Sometimes I just use 90% isopropyl alcohol.

Pic 22 shows I've taped two pieces of paper over the holes after cleaning the box. This is a temporary measure to prevent air from blowing in while I gather everything that I'll be inserting several minutes later.

Pic 23 shows six jars of substrate waiting to be inoculated with the syringe. Each jar was wiped down with isopropyl alcohol immediately before being inserted through one of the box holes.

Pic 24 shows me inoculating the first jar. Note how high the box must be to fit the extended syringe as it's held above the jar. This box is 13 inches (33 cm) high without the lid attached.

Making a Flow Hood

A flow hood is a device which blows filtered air onto a workspace. The positive air pressure should be enough to consistently prevent dirty air particles (mold) from wafting into the workspace.

I created my flow hood with:

- a small, plastic storage container
- a small, USB-powered desk fan (specifically a TriPole Small Desk Fan USB Powered Portable Fan from Amazon)
- a HEPA filter (specifically a Guardian Technologies Germ Guardian Air Purifier Filter FLT4100 Genuine HEPA Replacement Filter from Amazon, with the following dimensions: 4.62"L x 1.5"W x 8.25"T
- a large food storage (sandwich) bag
- duct tape

Pics 25 and 26 (next page) show the final construction. I drilled out a hole slightly wider than the face of the filter surface. I taped the filter onto it making sure the filter faces the right direction for air flow.

Then I cut large holes on both sides of the sandwich bag. One side was taped to seal around the back of the HEPA filter. The other side was taped to seal around the frame of the desk fan. Essentially, a sealed space was created from the fan into the box.

It's a small workspace, but if I wipe down anything I introduce into it with isopropyl alcohol first, it works. I always run the fan at its highest setting.

Blue Thumb   Sean McNamara

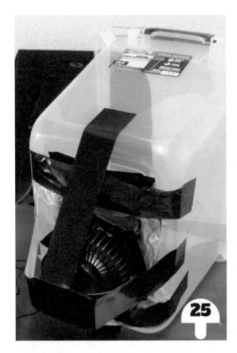
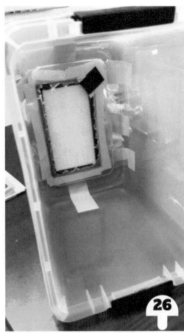

Pic 27 shows me introducing jars into the workspace in preparation for inoculation.

Making a Monotub

A *monotub* is a **clear plastic** container (including the lid) that you will use to initiate fruiting conditions once your mycelium has fully colonized the substrate. It will serve a double-purpose with Method 2 (bulk substrate) in that instead of using closed jars (Method 1 – PF Tek) during colonization, you will use the monotub itself.

During colonization for Method 2, you will create a high carbon dioxide environment by sealing all the holes with packing tape to prevent fresh air from entering.

Because of the need of a sealed space, make sure you purchase a storage container whose lid contains a *gasket*, a rubber liner to keep a tight, waterproof seal. Pic 28 shows a blue gasket on the inner rim of the lid.

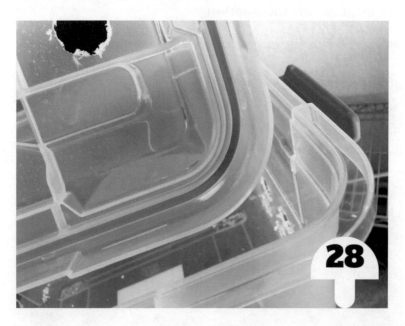

I drill the holes for my monotubs using a 1-inch drill bit, which you see in Pics 29 and 30.

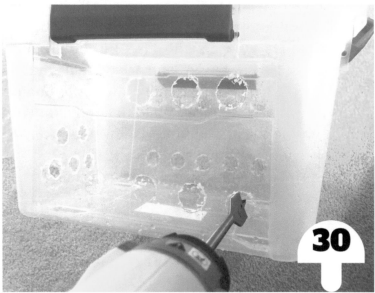

People sometimes refer to monotubs as *shotgun fruiting chambers*, but that is inaccurate. Shotgun fruiting chambers really look as if they've been hit by dozens of tiny ball bearings, entirely covering the walls and cover with very small holes.

In a monotub, rows of large holes are strategically drilled along the bottom edge of the container, and in rows along the cover. Sometimes another row is drilled along the upper edge of the walls.

The idea is to allow fresh air exchange to initiate fruiting after the substrate is fully colonized. When oxygen is introduced, this signals the mycelium to begin producing mushrooms. With holes in the cover and along the sides, air can move in and out of the container, letting carbon dioxide out and oxygen in.

Voice of Experience: If you decide to use Method 2 (bulk substrate) and attempt a second flush (discussed later), you will need to flood your monotub with a couple inches of water with the substrate floating in it.

The bottom holes in Pic 31 are high enough from the bottom to hold that much water. But I didn't plan ahead with the tub in Pic 34, and accidentally made the bottom holes too low to hold enough water to flood the substrate. For a second flush, I had to flood a different tub, transfer the substrate to it for a few hours, and then move it back to its original tub to fruit.

It wasn't a big problem, though, just an inconvenience.

Pics 31, 32, and 33 show the front, side, and top holes (stuffed with polyfill) of a **50-liter** container.

Pics 34, 35, and 36 show the front, side, and top holes (stuffed with polyfill) of an **18-liter** container.

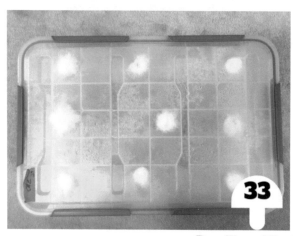

Part Two: The Essentials

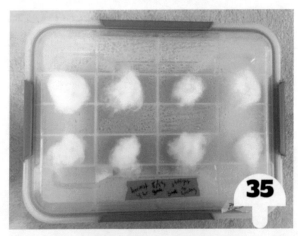

Blue Thumb   Sean McNamara

Part Two Equipment List

You will decide for yourself which of the following items you need based on which technique you choose to do after carefully reading the step-by-step instructions in each section.

Items will not be repeated. For example, tinfoil is listed in the Part Three equipment list. Therefore, it is not listed in the Part Four equipment list even though it is used with that technique as well.

FACE MASK

- for sterile working conditions

PSILOCYBIN SPORE SYRINGE

- order it from an online retailer

HUMIDIFIER

- a small one is sufficient

PRESSURE COOKER

- pressure cooker capable of reaching 15 PSI (pounds per square inch)

JAR PREP

- 12-pack of either 8-ounce or 16-ounce canning jars, depending on the size of your monotub

LID MODIFICATION

- hammer or mallet
- thick nail, spike, or awl
- pre-made self-healing injection ports or a tube of hi-temp RTV silicone sealant
- micropore disks or tape

STILL AIR BOX

- large, clear, plastic tub
- drill with a 1-inch drill bit

FLOW HOOD

- plastic box to serve as your workspace
- small desk fan
- HEPA filter
- large storage bag
- duct tape

MONOTUB

- clear plastic storage bin (the lid is also clear) whose lid comes with a gasket for air-tight sealing when closed
- polyester wadding/polyfill (craft and fabric stores carry this)

PART THREE:

PF TEK

Method 1: Growing on Cakes (PF Tek)

The *PF* in PF Tek stands for "Psilocybe Fanaticus." *Tek* is shorthand for "technique." This tek was developed by Robert McPherson, whose moniker is Psilocybe Fanaticus.

This tek has two major phases.

PHASE ONE: COLONIZING THE SUBSTRATE

In the first phase, jarfuls of mixed brown rice flower, water, and vermiculite are inoculated with spores, then colonized by the mycelium until they turn completely white. These enclosed clumps of mycelium are called *cakes*.

If you've never heard of **vermiculite**, it's a mineral used in gardening, often in potting mixes. We use it in PF Tek because it retains water well, and sufficient moisture is crucial.

It sometimes contains asbestos and it's not something you want to eat. As you'll see in the chapter *Cleaning Harvested Mushrooms*, you'll clean the vermiculite from your mushrooms before drying them.

PHASE TWO: FRUITING THE CAKES

In the second phase, the cakes are birthed out of their jars, then placed inside a monotub for the fruiting stage of the process, until it's time to harvest the mushrooms that grow from them.

Timeline from Start to Finish

Timelines are widely variable because the temperature, humidity, quality of ingredients, and grower's attention to detail also vary widely. Nevertheless, this timeline will give you some idea about what you can expect regarding time and tasks. This is assuming you have already set up either a still air box or a flow hood, have obtained a pressure cooker and canning jars, have modified the jar lids, and possess a spore syringe.

Specific growing instructions appear in the next section.

Day 1: Mix your substrate, fill the jars, then sterilize them in the pressure cooker.

Day 2: Inoculate your jars of substrate and store them someplace safe from extreme temperatures, in the dark.

3 to 6 weeks later: The spores become mycelium, which slowly spreads and colonizes the substrate in the jar, becoming a completely white cake.

After full colonization: Birth the cakes and dunk them in cold water in the refrigerator for 24 hours.

After being dunked for 24 hours: Place them inside the monotub.

10 days to three weeks later: *Pins* (think of them as baby mushrooms) appear on the surface of the cakes, then mature into fully grown mushrooms.

When mushrooms mature: Harvesting.
Mushrooms don't always mature at the same time, so you might harvest them individually over two or three days until the cakes are bare.

After harvesting: Attempt a second flush (optional).

Mixing the Substrate

RECIPE FOR PF TEK SUBSTRATE

You'll combine the following:

- one part of brown rice flour
- one part of water
- two parts vermiculite

You can usually find vermiculite in home-and-garden stores or hardware stores. If it's not currently gardening season where you live, you can order it online.

As for the brown rice flour, I choose organic food ingredients, but regular also works.

To measure a "part," just measure out in the same jars you'll be filling. In Pic 37, you see two parts of vermiculite (the two jars on the left), one part brown rice flour, and one part tap water.

_____ Start by pouring the vermiculite in a bowl *first* (Pic 38) and mixing with the water (Pic 39), **before** adding the brown rice flour. This way, the vermiculite can absorb as much of the water as it can on its own. This will ensure sufficient moisture in the jar for the duration of colonization.

_____Then mix in the brown rice flour (Pic 40).

_____Squeeze the mixture with your hand (Pic 41). Only a few drops of water should drip from your fist. This is called *field capacity*.

Too much water will cause mold to grow quickly. **Too little water** will be too dry for the mycelium to grow. So, testing for field capacity is important.

_____ Fill the jars **halfway** (Pic 42), but do NOT pack the mixture down. Leave it loose and uncompressed (Pic 43, left), which will make it easier for the mycelium to grow and spread.

The mix in this recipe (2 parts vermiculite, 1 part brown rice flour, 1 part water) should fill 6 jars (Pic 43, right). The jars should only be **filled half-way**.

Sterilizing Jars in the Pressure Cooker

_____After your jars are filled and the lids are screwed on, wrap a single layer of tin foil over the top of each to prevent water from dripping in through the micropore tape during the sterilization process.

_____Put the jars in the pressure cooker (Pic 44). If you ever sterilize a large number of jars, it's alright to stack them if they don't all fit on one layer. Just make sure there's no possibility of the pressure-release valves from being blocked from the inside.

_____Pour some water into the pressure cooker, enough to come up three or four inches from the bottom of the cooker.

_____Place it on your stove. Lock the lid closed all the way, then turn the heat to *high*.

_____When the gauge says you've reached 15 PSI (pounds per square inch) the rocker will start rocking and being noisy. Lower the heat to *medium-high*. It usually takes around 20-25 minutes to build up to 15 PSI (Pic 45).

_____Once the cooker has reached 15 PSI, set a timer for 90 minutes. Check the gauge every few minutes until you're familiar with your cooker. If the rocker stops making noise, it means the cooker has cooled down, and you should turn the heat up again to keep it at 15 PSI.

_____At 90 minutes, turn OFF the heat and **let the pressure cooker sit exactly where it is on your**

stove overnight, without opening the lid. It will be very hot and pressurized for many hours – don't touch it!

To maintain perfect sterility for a long as possible, it's best to leave the pressure cooker closed until you're ready to inoculate the jars with your liquid culture syringe.

If you are in a hurry and want the jars to cool down as quickly as possible the next morning, take them out of the pressure cooker and put them on a clean counter or table. Even though the jars may feel like they've reached room temperature, you should check with a thermometer if you have one (don't open the jars though).

If you don't have a thermometer and you're not sure, wait a few more hours. Pic 46 shows the jars are still too hot to be inoculated. Pic 47 shows they've nearly reached room temperature. I usually wait a couple more hours to be sure the substrate in the center of the jar has also cooled down. Remember, **if the substrate is too hot** when you inoculate it, the mycelium won't grow.

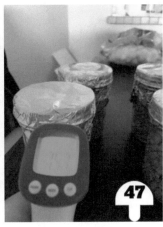

Inoculating the Jars

_____ Set up your workspace, someplace clean. Make sure you're wearing a facemask, clean clothes, and have washed your hands very well and/or wear nitrile gloves.

_____Put on your facemask.

_____Whether you're using a flow hood or a still air box, wipe the inner surfaces with 70% or 90% isopropyl alcohol. If using a flow hood, turn on the fan before you begin wiping it down to create positive air pressure.

Workspace Policy: Every time you introduce an object into your still air box or flow hood, clean it with isopropyl alcohol first.

_____ Before introducing the spore syringe into your workspace, shake it vigorously for several minutes to break up and distribute any chunks of spores inside of it. If you look carefully, the spores will appear like tiny black or dark indigo specks in the fluid (Pic 3, pg. 21). Shake it like vigorously until any clumps are broken up and the spores are distributed as much as possible.

_____ Wipe down your syringe (not the needle since it has a cap you'll pull off before use) and place it inside the flow hood.

_____ Wipe down your first jar just outside the flow hood, place it inside the flow hood, and remove the tin foil (Pic 27, pg. 40).

_____ Uncap the syringe, pierce it through the self-healing injection port (Pic 49, next page). **Read the next step *before* injecting any spores.**

_____ Don't touch the flour-vermiculite substrate with the needle. After inserting the needle through the self-healing injection port, point the needle straight down, angled toward the edge of the glass (Pic 50, next page).

Inject 1 to 1.5 cc's of spore fluid onto the substrate where it meets the glass. Injecting directly beneath the port will make it easy for you to find the mycelium when it becomes visible after a week or so.

Part Three: PF Tek

Blue Thumb   Sean McNamara

Voice of Experience: Sometimes the liquid appears clear as you inject it, and sometimes dark chunks of spores will shoot out. Either is fine. Even the clear liquid contains spores. However, you may notice young mycelium in jars injected with chunks becoming visible much sooner than in jars where the injected fluid appeared clearer.

_____ Place the inoculated jar on the table nearby. It **does not** need to be kept in the flow hood or still air box after inoculation.

_____ Set the syringe down inside the flow hood, if necessary, but without touching the needle to the workspace's surface.

_____Wipe down the next jar with alcohol before introducing it to your workspace and repeat the process until all your jars are inoculated.

See Pic 24 on pg. 37 for an example of inoculating jars inside a still air box.

Mycelium Colonization

_____ Place the jars someplace dark at or near room temperature (between 65 and 72 degrees if possible).

_____ Consider putting some masking tape on each jar and writing their inoculation date on it so you can track their progress. Or use the sample tracking sheet in Part Eight. You can expect to see the soft, subtle strands of the mycelium growing after one week. Over time, it'll spread like a spider web. When it grows on the top surface it may appear fuzzy.

The cakes inside the jars will be ready for _birthing_ once they are all fully colonized (entirely white). It's normal for some to grow faster than others. If one is fully colonized, it's okay to make it stay in the jar a few extra days while the others catch up.

Pic 51 shows the earliest days of mycelium's growth.

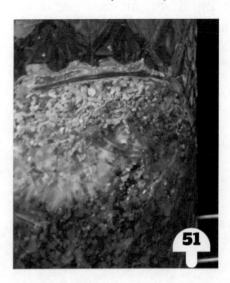

Pic 52 shows a half-way colonized jar.

In Pic 53, we see mycelium on the bottom of the jar.

When all the jars are fully colonized, it's time to *birth the cakes*. Some cakes will colonize several days faster than others. It's fine to let them wait in their jars, while the rest catch up.

Part Three: PF Tek

Be aware: Any jars with blue, green, or other colors have mold growing inside them.

Don't open moldy jars inside your home, or the mold will circulate in the air. Dispose of them in the garbage, or if you have a yard, you can open the jars outside and bury the cakes in the earth.

Some growers have reported healthy mushrooms growing after infected substrate was buried in good growing conditions (good temperature, shade, moisture).

Birthing, Dunking, and Rolling Your Cakes

BIRTHING YOUR CAKES

_____Put on your facemask.

_____ Prepare one or more large pots of cold water. You'll be submerging your cakes in the fridge overnight. You can put several cakes in the same pot or bowl if it's big enough.

_____ Wipe down the jars and lids with alcohol and wash your hands and/or wear sterile gloves.

_____ Open the first jar, turn it upside down, and gently smack the bottom enough times to make the cake slide out. Catch it as gently as possible in your hand.
Pic 54 on the next page shows the hand positions when birthing a cake. Notice the bottom hand allows space for the cake to emerge.

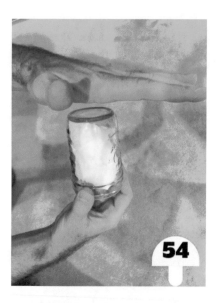

_____Grasp the cake gently with only two or three fingers, placing it in the water (Pic 55).

_____Then, open the second jar and repeat. Continue until all the cakes are floating in the water.

Blue Thumb   Sean McNamara

Voice of Experience: No matter how gentle you are, the mycelium will *bruise* from being handled. Bruising appears within minutes and will appear blue gray. There's no need to worry, though. Your mushrooms will still grow. Bruises are **not** mold.

DUNKING YOUR CAKES

_____ Use inverted lids, plates, or other things to press the cakes beneath the surface of the water since they float. Don't use something which will squash the cake down against the bottom of the pot or bowl. You merely want to submerge it, so it absorbs as much water as possible.

_____ If possible, leave the cakes in the refrigerator for twenty-four hours. But even twelve or eighteen hours are beneficial.

PREPARE YOUR MONOTUB BEFORE PULLING CAKES FROM THE FRIDGE

_____ Soak enough perlite in a large bowl to fill the bottom of the monotub with about an inch of perlite. **Like vermiculite, perlite holds water well. In a monotub, perlite releases it slowly into the air to maintain humidity.** Give it a few minutes to absorb as much water as possible before draining it and spreading it evenly inside the monotub (Pic 56).

Pic 57 shows a handful of soaked perlite, up close.

Blue Thumb   Sean McNamara

_____ Clean the inside surface your monotub and its lid with isopropyl alcohol.

_____ Drain the perlite and pour it inside your monotub, smoothing it out to make a level surface.

_____ Insert clean polyfill fiber into the holes in the sides and lid of the monotub (Pics 58 and 59).

_____ Cut small squares or circles out of tinfoil, one for each cake, and lay them out inside the monotub. Position them away from the walls so future mushrooms have enough space to grow without touching the container's surfaces. The cakes should fit onto their tinfoil pads, so they don't touch the perlite. See cakes on their tinfoil pads on pg. 73.

_____ Once your monotub is ready, put the lid on. It's important to expose it to as little air as possible to remove the chances of mold flying in and growing.

ROLLING THE CAKES

_____ Prepare a small plate with a layer of dry vermiculite. Start with one cup's worth and add more if necessary.

_____ When you take a cake out of the water, roll it gently on the vermiculite while it's still wet, then sprinkle some so the top and bottom are also covered (Pics 61 and 62).

They don't have to be perfect or 100% covered, just mostly. Overworking the cake at this stage will lead to more bruising, and it's better to get it in the monotub quickly so mold in the air doesn't attach itself to it while it's out.

_____ Place the rolled cakes on their tinfoil inside the monotub, as seen in Pics 63 and 64.

Initiating Fruiting

_____ Using a spray bottle, mist the sides of the container (inside), as well as the lid with tap water. Be careful not to spray the cakes directly. This can cause bruising and promote mold growth. The purpose of misting the sides of the box is to maintain humidity.

_____ After misting, put the lid on.

_____ Place the monotub someplace where there is ambient light, but away from direct sunlight. If it gets too hot in the monotub, it could overheat the mycelium (killing it) or promote mold growth. Using ordinary room lights or desk lamps along with the ambient light from a nearby window works perfectly fine.

_____ You might consider purchasing a _hygrometer_ to monitor the temperature and humidity _inside_ the monotub. With a large digital display, you'll be able to read it easily by looking through the tub instead of needing to open the lid to read it. Humidity should read above 80% inside the tub.

Choose one with a magnetic back so you can use magnets to stick it to the inside of the tub by placing strong magnets on the outside of the tub's wall to hold it in place (Pics 65 and 66). Clean the hygrometer with isopropyl alcohol before attaching it inside the tub.

Voice of Experience: I stopped using a hygrometer a while ago. I realized if my home's ambient temperature was comfortable for me, then it would be comfortable for mycelium and mushrooms. Regular misting (next section) ensured proper humidity.

Blue Thumb   Sean McNamara

_____ Record the date you put your cakes into *fruiting conditions* by either putting masking tape on the tub and writing on it, or by using the tracking sheet in Part Eight.

_____ Give the monotub daily light and dark cycles (turn the lights out in the evening and while you sleep). Don't worry about keeping the cycles exactly to twelve hours of light and twelve hours of dark.

Let the monotub "sleep when you sleep," and be "awake" when you are.

Pic 67 shows my first monotub. I positioned it near the north-facing glass doors to my patio for indirect sunlight. I set it on a chair to keep it off the floor, away from critters. I also used a reading lamp but kept it far enough above the lid so as not to overheat the tub.

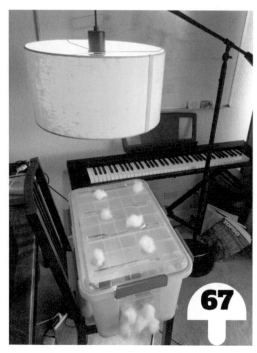

DAILY FANNING AND MISTING

During colonization (before fruiting, inside the jars), mycelium breathes carbon dioxide.

But **fruiting is initiated with oxygen**. In nature, underground mycelium grows upward toward the surface. Once it's close enough, the exposure to oxygen at the shallow depth triggers the fruiting process, and the mushrooms eventually break through the surface.

_____Put on your facemask and wash your hands.

_____ Twice per day, once every morning, and once every night, open the container and use the lid to gently fan fresh air into the box for 30 seconds. Don't breathe into the box, don't let your dog or cat near the box when the lid is open. Dander can carry mold.

Pics 68, 69, 70, and 71 on the next page show me slowly wafting the lid over the monotub to introduce fresh air (oxygen). Here, I was posing for the photo, so I forgot to put my mask on.

Pic 72 shows how the sides of the monotub should appear after misting them. **Water should not pool** on the bottom along the edges, as this invites mold growth.

_____ If, and **only if**, the sides and lid of the box are dry, use your spray bottle to mist them until drops of water cling to them. If they are still wet from the previous spraying, don't spray. Over spraying only invites mold growth.

Also, letting your box **go dry too long will prevent** mushroom growth since mushrooms are 90% water.

For extra precautions against prolonged dryness, see Pics 1 and 2 on pg. 16.

PINNING

After a couple weeks, baby mushrooms will appear, called *pins*. These are little dark cylindrical knobs growing out of the mycelium. Right before this stage, you might notice the mycelium getting thicker, developing *knots*, bumps, or a ropy texture on the sides. These eventually form into pins. The pins will mature into full mushrooms within a week or two after their appearance.

Pics 73, 74, and 75 show pins. They are often difficult to distinguish from thick clusters of vermiculite when they have just emerged. But this usually happens while you sleep ☺.

Blue Thumb   Sean McNamara

Pics 76, 77, 78, and 79 show pins growing into juvenile mushrooms, before their caps form.

82

Blue Thumb   Sean McNamara

Pic 80 shows a pin which grew *in vitro* (inside the jar) during the colonization process. It's next to the last joint of my pinky finger for perspective.

If you find a pin on your cake when you birth it from the jar, leave it in place. Dunk and roll the cake as usual and it's quite possible for the pin to continue maturing into a healthy mushroom.

You'll learn how to fruit in vitro <u>on purpose</u> later in this section.

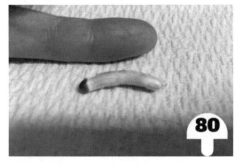

Pics 81, 82, 83, 84, 85, and 86 show mushrooms approaching maturity.

Blue Thumb   Sean McNamara

The growth of the mushrooms in Pics 83, 84 and 85 occurred over two days.

Blue Thumb   Sean McNamara

The mushrooms in Pic 85 grew so much quicker than the others in the monotub, I had to harvest them before the others were ready. The cake in the back left of Pic 86 shows the exposed mycelium from where I plucked the large mushroom.

Harvesting

Over time, the mushrooms will fully mature. The caps will spread open, tearing the *veil* beneath the cap so the spores waiting inside the gills can be released.

I recommend harvesting them before the spores are released, otherwise your tub will be a mess.

If you have allergies or are sensitive to microscopic airborne particles, preventing spores from being released into your living space is very important.

In Pic 87, the caps are just about to widen, then tear away from their veils. This is a great time to harvest unless you want to take a spore print (see Part Six).

Blue Thumb   Sean McNamara

The growth from Pic 88 to Pic 89 took place in a matter of hours. Notice the veils tearing away in Pics 89 and 90.

Blue Thumb   Sean McNamara

Mushrooms can go from almost open to full spore release within several hours. If you're going to sleep and you suspect they could dump spores before you wake up the next day, it's best to go ahead and harvest them.

Reach into the monotub with a clean hand and/or wear gloves. Grab the mushrooms at the base, where they emerge from the mycelial surface of the cake. Use a gentle twisting motion to tear them away without damaging the mycelium too much.

You could also cut them off the cake with a paring knife or a scalpel, as I did with the mushrooms in Pic 92.

Part Three: PF Tek

Second Flush

After you've completely harvested a cake, you can dunk it again for twenty-four hours in the fridge, the same way you did it the first time and try for a *second flush*, a second crop of mushrooms.

But **after the second dunk, don't roll your cakes in vermiculite again**. The first time you rolled them, the mycelium was pristine and free of undesirable organisms. Covering them with vermiculite was a form of protection.

Over the last couple of weeks, some germs have undoubtedly wafted into the tub, mostly while fanning it, but landed on the vermiculate where they couldn't grow. If you roll the cakes in vermiculite now, it'll enclose those germs beneath a moistened layer of vermiculite, hugging them closer to the mycelium where they'll begin to feed and spread.

Just return the cakes just as they are after the dunk to their tinfoil pads in the monotub, then fan daily as usual. Mist the tub as usual, only when the condensation on the walls of the monotub has dried up. Your cakes soaked up a lot of water during their second dunk, so over spraying the tub now brings an extra risk of mold.

It's normal for the cake to appear even more bruised in the monotub after a second dunk, but that's okay, just try to be as gentle as possible.

A second dunk *may or may not* produce a second flush. Give the cakes a couple of weeks to produce pins before deciding to toss them out.

Fruiting In Vitro

Fruiting *in vitro* means fruiting the mycelium while it's still inside the jar. Instead of birthing the cake after it's fully colonized, you would do the following:

_____Put on your facemask and wash your hands.

_____Before taking off the jar's lid, clean the jar and the lid with isopropyl alcohol.

_____Place the jar inside a monotub prepared with soaked perlite. In Pic 93, two in vitro cakes share a tub with a natural, *in vivo* cake.

94

Pic 94 is a closeup of the top of one of the jars. The mycelium is forming *primordium* and *hyphal knots*, precursors to pins.

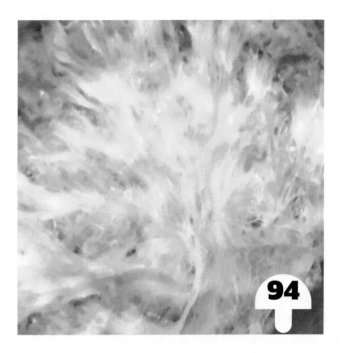

Pic 95 shows young pins emerging.

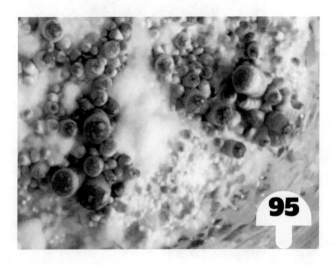

Pic 96 shows growing pins. The exposed cake hasn't produced any pins yet.

Pic 97 shows even larger pins.

At a certain point, I intuited it was time to birth the cake and give the pins room to expand (Pic 98).

I placed the cake on a fresh piece of tinfoil (Pic 99, 100, and 101).

Part Three: PF Tek

In Pic 102, the cakes are nearly ready for harvesting.

Voice of Experience: Do you wonder what happened to the natural cake that shared the monotub with the in vitro ones? It never produced any pins.

I was curious to understand why, so I cut it in half. It was almost completely dry to the touch inside. Is it possible the monotub wasn't as humid as it should have been? Perhaps the in vitro cakes succeeded because the glass enclosure helped them retain moisture.

Part Three Equipment List

You will decide for yourself which of the following items you need based on which technique you choose to do after carefully reading the step-by-step instructions in this section.

These are in addition to items already mentioned in earlier lists which you may need here.

- brown rice flour

- vermiculite

- tinfoil

- electric thermometer

- isopropyl alcohol

- perlite

- hygrometer and magnets

- spray bottle for misting water

- gloves for sterile work conditions

PART FOUR:

BULK SUBSTRATE

Method 2: Growing on Bulk Substrate

Note: The following instructions assume you have already read Part Three: PF Tek.

Growing mushrooms on bulk substrate is a method which typically yields more mushrooms per flush than PF Tek cakes do. However, it takes longer because it involves two periods of incubation and colonization instead of one.

It's also a bit messier than PF Tek, since you'll really use your hands when mixing the bulk substrate. For some growers, this is enriching and a lot of fun. Using one's hands this way contributes an earthy quality to mushroom cultivation.

Growing with bulk substrate has four major phases.

PHASE ONE: MAKING GRAIN SPAWN

In the first phase, the primary substrate is prepared, sterilized, inoculated, and colonized, just like with PF Tek, from Part Three.

But instead of using a mixture of brown rice flour and vermiculite, the primary substrate is typically one of several choices of grain and is therefore called *grain spawn*. Growers choose between rye grain, wheat berries, or even bird seed.

I prefer to use popcorn, so that is the type of grain spawn featured in this guide. Therefore, the method we're using is called *Popcorn Tek*. The downside to popcorn is the shape of the kernels slows down colonization. Since they're so round, less of each kernel's surface touches the surrounding kernels.

Therefore, there's less surface for mycelium to travel on to get from one kernel to the next.

The upside to using popcorn is that its nutritional profile makes it less prone to mold infestation. Rye grain, on the other hand, is richer in nutrients and offers more surface area for mycelial expansion, but mold has a much greater chance of proliferating on it than on popcorn.

I hate wasting time and energy, so I choose popcorn for its reduced probability of contracting mold. Also, popcorn is cheap and widely available in any grocery store. I don't mind spending a little more for the organic stuff, though.

PHASE TWO: MAKING BULK SUBSTRATE

Phase two occurs when the grain spawn is fully colonized. Bulk substrate, with which the grain spawn will be combined, needs to be prepared.

Bulk substrate can be made from various media. Bulk substrate is used to expand the mycelium by growing it on moistened plant fibers that have either been pasteurized or sterilized.

In this guide, you'll learn to use substrate composed of **coco coir** (dried coconut husk) mixed with vermiculite and water. You can find coco coir at your local hydroponic or mushroom cultivation supply store, home-and-garden stores, and online.

Many people pasteurize their bulk substrate. This involves putting the dried material in a bucket, pouring boiling water into it, then putting a lid on the bucket.

It's then insulated by being wrapped with towels or blankets and allowed to sit overnight.

The logic behind pasteurization is that the substrate is too low in nutritional value to promote the proliferation of any mold or other germs that may already be present inside it, making full sterilization unnecessary. Some argue that sterilization eliminates the beneficial microbiome existent in the substrate. I'm not sure where I stand on that at this point.

I prefer to sterilize my substrate for four reasons. First, I already own a pressure cooker so I might as well use it.

Second, I'm so unwilling to risk mold growth that I'm happy to sterilize the substrate.

Third, sterilization doesn't take much longer than pasteurization. They both take many hours to cool down to room temperature, usually overnight.

Fourth, I figured out a way to prepare bulk substrate in a way that does not result in a huge sloppy mess inside my pressure cooker, which you'll learn here.

PHASE THREE: COLONIZING BULK SUBSTRATE

In this phase, the colonized grain spawn is mixed with the sterilized and cooled bulk substrate. Mixing them serves to inoculate the bulk substrate because the mycelium from the grain spawn treats the bulk substrate as a new food source and spreads throughout. This phase takes ten days.

PHASE FOUR: FRUITING THE BULK SUBSTRATE

 Once the bulk substrate is fully colonized, you will initiate fruiting by allowing fresh air exchange, fanning, and misting the monotub twice or three times a day. Pins will eventually appear. Around a week after their appearance, they will transform into mushrooms.

Timeline from Start to Finish

This timeline assumes you have all the same equipment listed in the timeline for PF Tek in the previous section.

Specific growing instructions appear in the next section.

Day 1: Soak the uncooked corn kernels in plain, room temperature water for 24 hours.

Day 2: Boil and simmer the kernels, air-dry them, and sterilize them inside the canning jars.

Day 3: Inoculate the jars the same way you did with PF Tek.

3 to 6 weeks later: The spores become mycelium, which slowly spreads and colonizes the corn in the jar, becoming a completely white cake (although the corn gives the gossamer mycelium a golden hue).

When the grain spawn (corn) is fully colonized: Mix the bulk substrate (coco coir, vermiculite, and water), put it into canning jars, and sterilize them.

The day after bulk sterilization: Combine and mix the fully colonized grain spawn with the sterilized bulk substrate inside the monotub.

10 days: Incubate the monotub to colonize the bulk substrate with mycelium.

After 10 days: Initiate fruiting conditions for the monotub.

10 days to three weeks later: Pins will appear on the surface of the bulk substrate, then mature into fully grown mushrooms.

When mushrooms mature: Harvesting. Mushrooms don't always mature at the same time, so you might harvest them individually over two or three days until the substrate is bare.

After harvesting: Attempt a second flush (optional). Third and fourth flushes are also possibilities.

Preparing the Primary Substrate: Grain Spawn

INGREDIENTS FOR *POPCORN TEK*

You'll need the following:

- one 28-ounce bag of popcorn kernels
- tap water
- food-grade gypsum powder (optional)

One 28-ounce bag (Pic 103) will fill 4 large wide-mouth jars half-way (which is how much you will fill your jars before putting them in the pressure cooker).

4 large jars' worth is enough grain spawn if you're using a smaller monotub, such as 18 liters (19 quarts). If you're using a larger monotub, like 50 liters (53 quarts), then you'll want to use 8 half-filled jars of grain spawn (corn).

In this guide, we'll assume you're using the smaller monotub.

_____Fill 4 wide-mouthed jars half-way with corn kernels (Pic 104).

_____Pour the corn from the 4 jars into a large pot, then add enough tap water to cover the kernels with one inch (2.5 cm) of water (Pic 105). Then soak for 24 hours. This will allow the kernels to absorb the water they'll need to maintain enough moisture in the jar during colonization.

_____Strain the kernels, then bring a fresh pot of water to a boil. Add the kernels to the boiling water and bring it down to a high simmer (Pic 106). Simmer for one hour, or until you can split a kernel by pressing your fingernail into it without much difficulty (Pic 107).

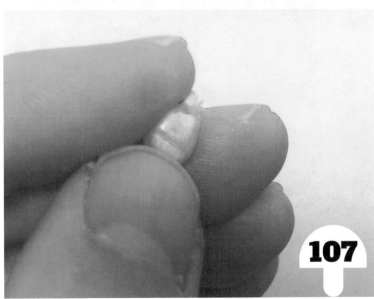

_____Once the kernels are tender, strain them (Pic 108). Then spread the kernels out on trays the exterior of the kernels can air-dry (Pic 109).

_____ Adding food-grade gypsum is optional. Since corn kernels are less nutritious for the mycelium than a grain like rye, sprinkling one or two tablespoons of gypsum over the corn (Pic 110) and mixing it in (Pic 111) can be beneficial. It should be a light dusting. Avoid clumps. The photos show a bit too much gypsum.

_____Fill your jars with the corn. Since the corn is swollen with water, it'll fill the jars more than it did when it was dry. It's alright if they're a bit more than half-way full.

Sterilizing the Grain Spawn

_____Put the jar lids on, cover them with tinfoil, and put the jars in the pressure cooker like you did with PF Tek (Pic 113).

_____Don't forget to add water to the pressure cooker, filling halfway up the outside of the jars.

_____Lock the lid closed all the way, then turn the heat to high.

_____When the gauge says you've reached 15 PSI (the rocker will start rocking and being noisy) lower the heat to medium-high. It usually takes around 20-25 minutes to build up to 15 PSI (Pic 45 on pg. 56).

Part Four: Bulk Substrate

_____Once the cooker has reached 15 PSI, set a timer for 90 minutes.

_____At 90 minutes, turn OFF the heat and let the pressure cooker sit exactly where it is on your stove **overnight, without opening the lid**. It will be very hot and pressurized for many hours – don't touch it!

To maintain perfect sterility for a long as possible, it's best to leave the pressure cooker closed until you're ready to inoculate the jars with your liquid culture syringe.

If you are in a hurry and want the jars to cool down as quickly as possible the next morning, take them out of the pressure cooker and put them on a clean counter or table. Even though the jars may feel like they've reached room temperature, you should check with a thermometer if you have one (don't open the jars though).

If you don't have a thermometer and you're not sure, wait a few more hours. Pic 46 on pg. 57 shows the jars are still too hot to be inoculated. Pic 47 shows they've nearly reached room temperature.

I usually wait a couple more hours to be sure the corn in the center of the jar also cools down. Remember, **if the corn is too hot** when you inoculate it, the mycelium won't grow.

Inoculation and Colonization

_____ Set up your workspace, someplace clean. Make sure you're wearing a facemask, clean clothes, and have washed your hands very well and/or wear nitrile gloves.

_____Put on your facemask.

_____Whether you're using a flow hood or a still air box, wipe the inner surfaces with 70% or 90% isopropyl alcohol. If using a flow hood, turn on the fan before you begin wiping it down (see Pic 48 on pg. 58).

Workspace Policy: Every time you introduce an object into your still air box or flow hood, clean it with isopropyl alcohol first.

_____ Before introducing the spore syringe into your workspace, shake it vigorously for several minutes to break up and distribute any chunks of spores inside of it. If you look carefully, the spores will appear like tiny black or dark indigo specks in the fluid (Pic 3, pg. 21). Shake it like crazy until it's mixed and distributed as much as possible.

_____ Wipe down your syringe (not the needle since it has a cap you'll pull off before use) and place it inside the flow hood.

Part Four: Bulk Substrate

_____ Clean your first jar and its lid with alcohol, place it inside the flow hood or still air box, and remove the tin foil.

_____ Uncap the syringe, pierce it through the self-healing injection port (Pic 114). **Read the next step *before* injecting any spores.**

_____ Don't touch the corn with the needle. After inserting the needle through the self-healing injection port, point the needle straight down, angled toward the edge of the glass.

Inject 1 to 1.5 cc's of spore fluid onto the corn where it meets the glass. Injecting right beneath the port will make it easy for you to find the mycelium when it becomes visible after a week or so. With corn, it usually appears on the kernels at the very bottom of the jar since much of the liquid dribbles down all the way.

Voice of Experience: Sometimes the liquid appears clear as you inject it, and sometimes dark chunks of spores will shoot out. Either is fine. Even the clear liquid contains spores. However, you may notice young mycelium in jars injected with chunks becoming visible sooner than in jars where the injected fluid appeared clearer.

_____ Place the inoculated jar on the table nearby. It **doesn't** need to be kept in the flow hood or still air box after inoculation.

_____ Set the syringe down inside the workspace, if necessary, but without touching the needle to the workspace's surfaces.

_____Wipe down the next jar with alcohol before introducing it to your workspace and repeat the process until all your jars are inoculated.

See Pic 24 on pg. 37 for an example of inoculating jars inside a still air box.

Mycelium Colonization

_____ Place the jars someplace dark at or near room temperature (between 65 and 72 degrees if possible).

_____ Consider putting some masking tape on each jar and writing their inoculation date on it so you can track their progress. Or use the sample tracking sheet in Part Eight. You can expect to see the soft, subtle strands of the mycelium growing after one week.

With corn, mycelium may first appear as a small, solid patch of white on the surface of a kernel, or between two touching kernels. Over time, it'll spread out across nearby kernels. When it grows on the top surface it may appear fuzzy, the same way it does with PF Tek.

The jars of corn will be ready for use once they are all fully colonized (entirely white). It's normal for some to grow faster than others. If one is fully colonized, it's okay to make it stay in the jar a few extra days while the others catch up.

Be aware: Any jars with blue, green, orange, or other colors have mold growing inside them.

Don't open these jars inside your home, or the mold will circulate in the air. Dispose of them in the garbage, or if you have a yard, you can open them outside and bury the cakes in the earth. Some growers have reported healthy mushrooms growing after infected substrate was buried in good growing conditions outside (good temperature, shade, moisture).

Pic 115 shows a fully colonized jar of corn. The golden hue is normal, it is NOT mold.

Preparing Bulk Substrate

Voice of Experience: I found out the hard way that many of the measurements for bulk substrate found online and in YouTube videos are either wrong, leaving the substrate much too wet, or they make you accidentally produce too much substrate for a single monotub, leading to excessive waste.

Because of that, I developed this technique for measuring the ingredients and sterilizing them.

The measurements below are for a small monotub, utilizing 4 jars of grain spawn.

If you are using a larger monotub, use your intuition and basic math skills to increase the proportions accordingly. For example, for a large tub, I used 75 grams instead of 50 grams, and added more water to reach *field capacity*.

INGREDIENTS FOR BULK SUBSTRATE

Since we're **assuming you are using 4 jars of grain spawn (corn) in a small monotub**, see Pic 116), you'll need the following:

- 50 grams of coco coir
- 50 grams of vermiculite
- 1 tablespoon of food-grade gypsum powder (optional)
- tap water

_____When using a container to measure ingredients on an electronic scale, don't forget to *tare* the scale (zero it out with the container on it). See Pic 117.

Part Four: Bulk Substrate

_____Measure 50 grams of dried coco coir, then set it aside.

_____Pour half a jarful of water into a bowl (Pic 119).

_____Add the coco coir to the water (Pic 120), and hand mix it. If more water is needed to soften and break apart the coco coir, add just enough.

_____Measure 50 grams of vermiculite (Pic 121).

Part Four: Bulk Substrate

_____Add the vermiculite to the wet coco coir, and thoroughly mix by hand (Pic 122).

_____Test the mixture's *field capacity* by squeezing a fistful (Pic 123). A few drops of water should emerge. If it's too dry, add more water and mix. If it's too wet, add a little more vermiculite.

Blue Thumb   Sean McNamara

_____ Fill 3 jars with the bulk substrate (Pic 124) and prepare them for sterilization by putting the lids on and covering with tinfoil (Pic 125).

Sterilizing Bulk Substrate

_____Pour three or four inches of water into the pressure cooker.

_____Put in the three jars of bulk substrate (Pic 126).

_____Lock the lid closed all the way, then turn the heat to high.

_____When the gauge says you've reached 15 PSI (the rocker will start rocking and being noisy) lower the heat to medium-high. It usually takes around 20-25 minutes to build up to 15 PSI (Pic 45 on pg. 57).

_____Once the cooker has reached 15 PSI, set a timer for 90 minutes

_____At 90 minutes, turn OFF the heat and let the pressure cooker sit exactly where it is on your stove **overnight, without opening the lid**. It will be very hot and pressurized for many hours – don't touch it!

To maintain perfect sterility for a long as possible, it's best to leave the pressure cooker closed until you're ready to combine the bulk substrate with the grain spawn inside the monotub.

If you are in a hurry and want the jars to cool down as quickly as possible the next morning, take them out of the pressure cooker and put them on a clean counter or table. Even though the jars may feel like they've reached room temperature, you should check with a thermometer if you have one (don't open the jars though).

If you don't have a thermometer and you're not sure, wait a few more hours. Pic 46 on pg. 57 shows the jars are still too hot to be inoculated. Pic 47 shows they've nearly reached room temperature.

I usually wait a couple more hours to be sure the substrate in the center of the jar also cools down. Remember, **if the bulk substrate is too hot** when you combine it with grain spawn, the mycelium will die.

Preparing the Monotub

Now that your grain spawn (corn) is fully colonized inside the jars, and the bulk substrate (coco coir and vermiculite) are sterilized, it's time to prepare the monotub for incubation and bulk colonization.

_____Seal all the holes in the sides and lid of the monotub with packing tape (Pic 127). I like to fold over the end of the tape at one end, so it doesn't stick to the tub. This makes it easy to grasp and pull the tape off later (Pic 128).

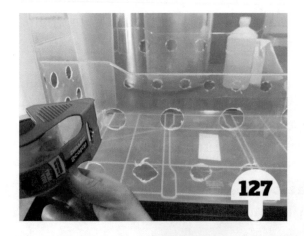

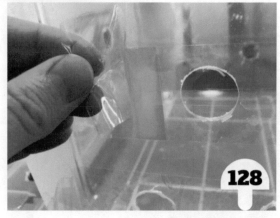

_____Wash the inside of the monotub with soap and hot water. Then clean the bottom, sides, and lid of the monotub with isopropyl alcohol (Pic 129).

_____Once the monotub is dried of all the alcohol, close the lid until it's time to add the grain spawn (colonized corn jars) and bulk substrate.

Combining Spawn and Substrate

_____It's time to combine the 4 jars of colonized corn with 3 jars of sterilized bulk substrate (Pic 130). Make sure the bulk substrate has completely cooled down to room temperature before continuing.

_____Put on your facemask.

_____Clean the jars and their lids with isopropyl alcohol (Pic 131).

_____ Open the monotub. Then one by one, open the jars of colonized corn and gently *birth* the corn into the monotub. Pic 132 shows the top of the corn inside an open jar.

Part Four: Bulk Substrate

_____Pic 133 shows a birthed cake of corn.

_____Pic 124 shows a larger monotub filled with 8 corn cakes.

_____ Gently crumble the corn cakes (Pic 135).

_____ Pour only two jars of the substrate onto the corn (Pic 136), and gently mix them together.

Part Four: Bulk Substrate

_____Gently form the mix into a mound. Allow at least one inch (2.5 cm) of space from the edges of the mound to the walls of the monotub (Pic 137).

Voice of Experience: Some growers suggest inserting a plastic liner inside the tub before filling it with spawn and substrate. Their reasoning is it will reduce *side pinning*. I personally dislike the idea of using single-use plastic or garbage bags, etc. in mushroom cultivation.

By forming the mound by leaving space between it and the monotub's walls, mushroom that grow on the edges have plenty of room to move and expand. The important thing is to avoid over spraying when fanning and misting and accidentally pooling water along the edges, which could promote mold growth.

_____ Gently sprinkle the final jar of sterilized substrate over the top and sides of the mound. Don't press it in but make an evenly dispersed top layer with it (Pic 138).

138

Voice of Experience: Pic 139 is from when I used a substrate recipe and measurements from a mushroom blogger's site. In this case, I ended up with too much bulk substrate, and it was too wet.

To remedy the situation, I simply squeezed out the excess water fistful by fistful to achieve field capacity as I added it to the monotub.

Pic 140 shows how I knew how much bulk substrate to add. I started by putting all the grain spawn on one side of the tub. Then I eyeballed an equal amount of bulk substrate on the other side, and then mixed them together (Pics 140 and 141). The I sprinkled more substrate to form a top layer.

Sean McNamara

_____After adding the top layer of bulk substrate, spray the walls and lid of the monotub with water, but not so much that it pools at the bottom. Also spray a little bit of water directly onto the top layer to replace any moisture lost over the last several minutes while being exposed to the air (Pic 142). Then close the lid.

Bulk Incubation and Colonization

_____The monotub is now sealed with tape over the holes and a closed lid. The bulk substrate inside needs time and carbon dioxide for the mycelium from the corn to spread throughout the rest of the substrate.

You might put a piece of tape on the monotub marking the date you put in into incubation or use the tracking sheet in Part Eight.

The substrate should be sufficiently colonized ten days from then, so mark your calendar.

Ideally, the tub will be stored somewhere away from extreme temperatures and kept in the dark.

Pics 143, 144, and 145 show the mycelium spreading through the bulk substrate. I used a flashlight to take the photos since the monotub was still incubating in darkness.

Blue Thumb   Sean McNamara

Part Four: Bulk Substrate

Initiating Fruiting

Ten days after incubation began, your bulk substrate should be ready for you to initiate fruiting conditions. Pic 146 shows the colonized bulk substrate ten days after incubation.

Voice of Experience: Unlike the colonized cakes from PF Tek or the colonized grain spawn (corn), which appear almost completely white inside their jars, a colonized bulk substrate doesn't look completely white or 100% covered in mycelium when fruited.

Don't worry, the mycelium will continue growing and thickening in fruiting conditions until fully white.

_____Begin initiating fruiting conditions be removing the tape and replacing it with polyester wadding or polyfill (Pics 147, 148, and 149).

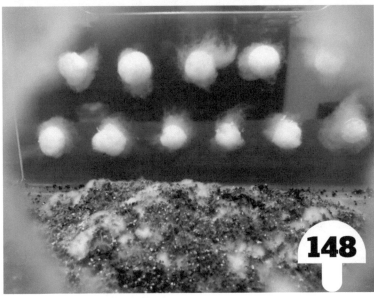

_____Spray the walls and lid of the monotub, taking care not to over spray or pool water along the edges (Pic 150).

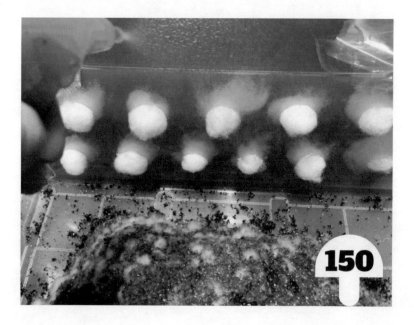

_____Twice each day, once in the morning and once at night, open the lid and fan the monotub with it, as we did with PF Tek (Pics 68, 69, 70, and 71 on pg. 77).

Over time, you will notice the mycelium becoming more dense and taking on a ropy texture (Pic 151. This is the formation of primordia and hyphal knots, from which pins will emerge.

Within a week or so of the mycelium forming primordia, the first pins will emerge (Pic 152 on pg. 144 and a closeup with Pic 153).

Part Four: Bulk Substrate

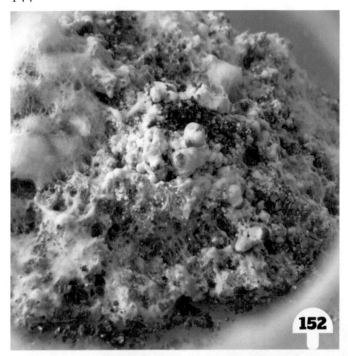

Blue Thumb   Sean McNamara

Over the next week or so, the pins will develop into juvenile mushrooms. The maturation from Pic 154 to Pic 155 occurred within twenty-four hours.

Pics 156 and 157 show the mushrooms several days later.

Voice of Experience: In Pic 158, we see that side pinning is not a problem when you formed the substrate mound with enough space between its edges and the monotub's walls. Also notice no water has pooled on the bottom, even though misting was done twice or three times each day, as needed. **No plastic liner needed.**

In Pics 159 and 160, we see that I didn't leave as much room along the edges in this monotub as I did in the earlier one. At first, I was nervous the mushrooms would suffer somehow.

Part Four: Bulk Substrate

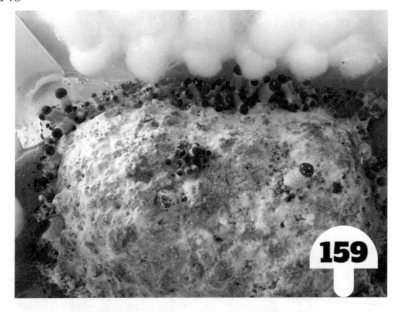

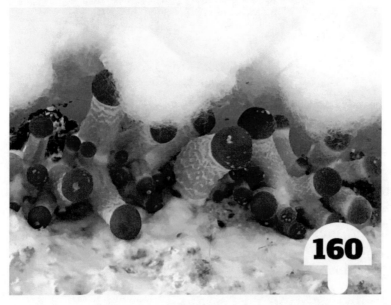

But as we see in Pics 161,162, and 163, there was **no need to worry**. The mushrooms managed just fine on their own.

Blue Thumb   Sean McNamara

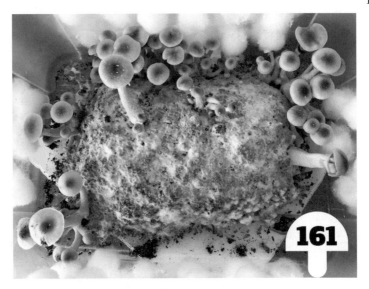

I suspect two reasons they grew concentrated on the edges. First, the mound was piled high, so the water it held may have seeped out toward the edges due to simple gravity and pressure. Second, the mycelium may have sensed the increased humidity closer to the walls due to spraying, and then it selected that region for pinning.

Part Four: Bulk Substrate

150

Pic 161may appear like this grow didn't produce that many mushrooms, but that isn't true. Pic 164 shows them harvested on a plate. Whether you are a microdoser or other type of user, this amount is more than enough to meet your needs for quite some time.

Blue Thumb   Sean McNamara

Harvesting

Pics 165 through 169 show mushrooms ready for harvesting in the previous monotub with plenty of space between the substrate's edge and the tub's walls.

167

168

Blue Thumb

Sean McNamara

Pic 170 shows where I cut a couple of mature mushrooms early for spore printing since the others weren't ready yet. Note the blue bruising along the cut on their *stipes*, also known as *stems* or *stalks*.

154

Time to harvest the rest of the monotub (Pic 171).

Second, Third, and Fourth Flushes

A second flush is when you put the harvested substrate back into fruiting conditions to get a second crop of mushrooms from it.

The first couple times I did this, I followed instructions I found online that told me I needed to first return the substrate to incubation for three days so the mycelium could rest. I will discuss this more later.

In Pic 172, we see a freshly harvested bulk substrate.

After harvesting the top of the bulk substrate, you can use something firm like a cutting board to lift it out of the monotub, as in Pic 173.

In Pics 174 and 175, we see there are still some pins to pluck around the edges before starting a second flush.

_____Carefully return the substrate to the monotub and pour enough water in to fill the tub just below the lowest hole, otherwise it'll spill out! (Pic 176).

You could also either gently pour water over the surface of the substrate, or generously use a spray bottle to wet it.

_____The substrate will tend to float on the water, but we want to submerge it so it soaks in as much as possible. Place something just heavy enough to press it beneath the surface without squashing it (Pic 177).

Pic 178 is a side view of the substrate soaking inside the tub.

Blue Thumb   Sean McNamara

_____Allow the substrate to soak in the water for at least 4 hours.

_____Use something firm and flat like a cutting board to carefully remove the substrate from the flooded tub, just like in Pic 173 and set it aside someplace clean.

_____Empty the monotub of water (Pic 179). Be careful, it could pour out the holes before it reaches the edge of the tub, spilling on your floor ☺

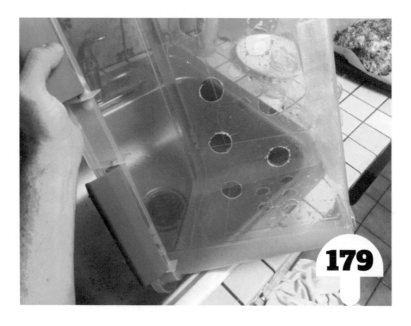

_____Gently replace the substrate inside the monotub.

_____**(Optional, read the *Voice of Experience* on pg. 161 before doing this and the next four steps related to incubations.)** Seal the holes with packing tape and close the lid.

_____Place the monotub (with holes sealed) in the same conditions you did when incubating and colonizing it the first time.

_____Record the date you returned it to incubation.

_____Three days later, take it out of incubation and initiate fruiting conditions by replacing the tape with polyfill, and commencing fanning and misting two to three times each day, as before.

____Within one to two weeks, you will have a second flush of mature mushrooms.

Pics 180 and 181 show the results of this substrate's second flush. The amount was about the same as the first flush.

Voice of Experience: One thing I noticed immediately after pulling the monotub out of its three-day incubation was the appearance of many ghostly gray, wiry-looking pins growing all over the substrate's surface.

I realized **the mushrooms had begun growing immediately after dunking the freshly harvested substrate in water for four hours**. The reason they looked so strange was that I'd starved them of oxygen after they'd begun growing rapidly.

This led me to believe **three days of incubation following a four-hour water dunk was unnecessary and perhaps detrimental.** To find out, I attempted a third flush with the same substrate.

This time, instead of putting into incubation for three days, I would immediately return it to fruiting conditions: fanning and misting every day, leaving the polyfill in the monotub's holes for continuous fresh air exchange.

Pic 182 shows a pin which emerged the very next day. Ghostly gray pins are in the background. That, and the rest of the grow the following week, showed me that **three-day incubation was unnecessary**.

Pics 183 and 184 show the results of the third flush. It was smaller yield, about one-third of normal, but still worth for the small amount of work needed to receive even more mushrooms from it.

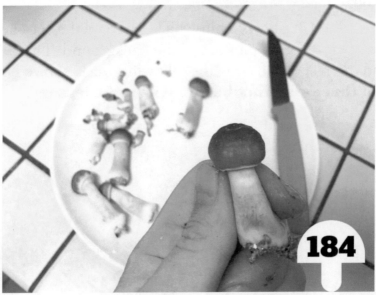

Sean McNamara

NO MORE 3-DAY INCUBATION FOR ME

I've stopped doing the 3-day incubation in between flushes. After a first flush, I flood the tub for four to six hours, then return the substrate to fruiting conditions, and begin seeing pins within a few days without the wiry, ghostly gray pins showing up.

Sometimes, pins appear the very next morning, if not several hours after being flooded.

IS A FOURTH FLUSH POSSIBLE?

The last time I had a third flush, I moved the monotub with the harvested substrate to another room. I fully intended to dispose of the substrate at my earliest convenience.

However, I completely forgot about that tub, and it sat ignored for several days until I remembered I needed to throw out the substrate.

To my surprise, I found healthy pins growing inside. So, I returned the tub to the other room and resumed fruiting conditions by fanning and misting it twice a day, as usual.

It produced fewer mushrooms than it did during the third flush, but many of them were significantly larger than those of earlier flushes. They made for beautiful spore prints.

So, yes, a fourth flush is possible.

I needed that monotub to start over with brand new substrate, so I haven't tried for a fifth flush yet. But I think it's possible.

Part Four Equipment List

You will decide for yourself which of the following items you need based on which technique you choose to do after carefully reading the step-by-step instructions in this section.

These are in addition to items already mentioned in earlier lists which you may need here.

- popcorn kernels

- coco coir

- clear packing tape

PART FIVE:

AFTER THE HARVEST

Cleaning Harvested Mushrooms

Some growers like to cut the mushrooms off at their base using a knife or scalpel. The advantage to doing it that way is you don't have to spend any time cleaning the bottom of the stipe of any vermiculite or other particles that usually stick to it. Therefore, they're already clean and ready to be dried or consumed.

But I prefer to (gently) tear my mushrooms from the substrate by hand, so I get the whole mushroom. Imagine if when cutting your mushroom with a blade you leave 10% of the mushroom's mass behind. I don't like the thought of that, or even of just 5%.

So, to receive as much of the mushroom tissue as possible, I take the whole thing and take the time cleaning each one by hand. A whole monotub's worth can take around 90 minutes to clean. But 90 minutes to save 5-10% of what's taken at least two months of effort and patience to achieve is a smart use of time.

To clean the mushrooms, dip the dirty ends in water and scrape the substrate off with a fingernail. The vermiculite sinks to the bottom while organic material floats. Pic 185 shows a dirty stipe next to a cleaned one.

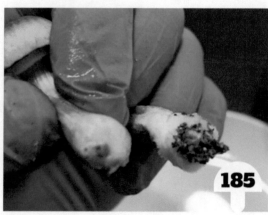

Blue Thumb   Sean McNamara

Pic 186 shows a monotub harvest before cleaning.
Pic 187 is the same harvest after cleaning.

I've even picked and cleaned all the pins, seen on
the left side of the plate. Note the gorgeous blue tint on
the stipes and pins, the results of being handled during
cleaning.

The Secret to High Potency

You might wonder why I would bother to pick all the tiny pins off the substrate during harvesting and spend the extra time cleaning and drying them with the mature mushrooms.

When you look at Pic 188, can you tell whether the little pin, the larger pin, or the mature mushroom has the most psilocybin in it? It's natural to assume the little pins couldn't possibly be as potent as the bigger fruits, but that could be incorrect.

It's possible for a pin to contain as much psilocybin as a mushroom. With a large mushroom, what you're getting more of is protein and water.

So, by cleaning and drying the pins and grinding them into powder along with the rest of the mushrooms and *mixing them all together*, I'm doing everything I can do to result in high potency.

For me, high potency isn't about tripping out. As a microdoser, it means I can take a smaller dose on my schedule to get the same psychological benefits, and my supply lasts longer. It's basic economics.

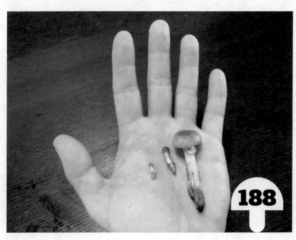

Blue Thumb   Sean McNamara

Pic 189 shows dirty pins floating in the cleaning bowl. Note the vermiculite and other unwanted substrate material has sunk to the bottom.

Pic 190 shows the cleaned pins.

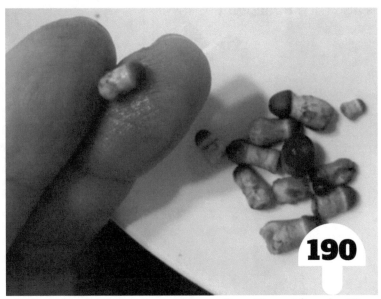

Voice of Experience: I don't know if psilocybin can enter through the skin while cleaning mushrooms. But I do know that when I have cleaned mushrooms bare handed, I've sometimes felt as I do when my microdose is slightly too much, or too strong.

Microdoses are *sub-perceptual,* meaning you shouldn't feel anything at all after consuming a microdose. When it's a bit too much, you can feel slightly "off" while still remaining completely sober and in full control of your faculties.

Therefore, I recommend wearing gloves while cleaning a complete harvest of mushrooms. But I must also admit that I've felt "off" even while wearing gloves, which tells me it is probably the *placebo effect,* a psychosomatic response that doesn't require external chemicals to produce strange sensations in the body.

Pic 191 shows a picture of my thumb after a morning of cleaning mushrooms without gloves. The blue bruise producing chemical had stained my skin. The picture was the inspiration for this book's title and was also used to design the cover.

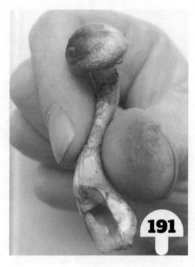

Blue Thumb   Sean McNamara

Drying Mushrooms

There are generally two ways to dry your mushrooms. First, you can lay them out on a paper towel and keep a fan blowing on them for several days until they are 100% cracker dry.

Cracker dry means they snap and crunch like a cracker when you break them in half. If they're still bendy or soft, that indicates there's still moisture in the tissue.

Storing them at this point (while still bendy or moist) could lead to rot, spoilage, or mold, wasting at least a couple months of your patient, diligent and delicate work.

The second, and faster, way is to use a vegetable dehydrator. Use the lowest heat setting and it'll only take a couple days to get them *cracker dry*, depending on the ambient humidity in your home and your geographical area.

Pic 192 shows a tray of freshly harvested and cleaned mushrooms in a vegetable dehydrator.

192

Pic 193 shows another tray from the same grow. Note the pins are placed on a paper towel to keep them from falling through the tray's holes when they shrink during the drying process.

Pic 194 on the next page shows how much mushrooms shrink when dried in the tray. Not pictured: the trays are covered with a lid with holes in it to allow the heated air to warm them while escaping through the top.

194

Part Five: After the Harvest

Pics 195, 196, 197, and 198 compare the same two mushrooms when fresh and dried. The scale reads 4.63 grams wet, and 0.23 grams dry.

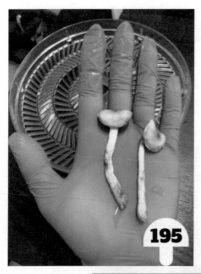
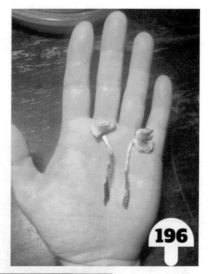

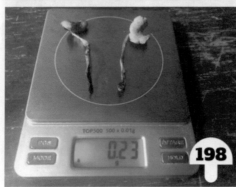

Blue Thumb   Sean McNamara

Long-Term Storage

Once the mushrooms are cracker-dry, one option is store them just as they are in an airtight container, in the dark, because ultraviolet light (sunlight) weakens potency over time. Insert a desiccant packet to help ensure dryness.

Pic 199 shows food-grade desiccant packets you can purchase online.

Pic 200 shows a basic sandwich bag with a desiccant packet inside.

Pic 201. One air-tight container inside another provides an extra layer of protection against humidity.

Pic 202 shows powdered mushrooms inside an amber-colored glass container with desiccant packet included.

Dried mushrooms can maintain potency for months, if not years, when kept in optimal storage conditions.

Making Mushroom Powder

Making mushroom powder is easy. All you need is an electric coffee or herb grinder, as in Pic 203.

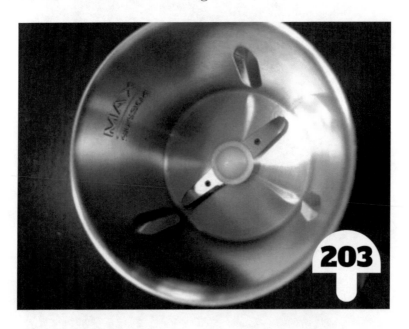

Pic 204 shows the cracker-dry mushrooms to be ground.

Blue Thumb   Sean McNamara

_____Put on your facemask when grinding mushrooms. When you open the lid, mushroom dust may fill the air, and you do not want to inhale mushroom dust. It won't make you hallucinate, it's just that breathing organic dust particles like that isn't good for anyone's lungs, especially if you have allergies or asthma.

Pic 205 shows the mushrooms ready for grinding.

Pic 206 shows the ground mushrooms. Follow your grinder's instructions about how long to run the grinder at one time before letting it cool down.

You can store your powder as shown in Pic 202, or you could also put it into capsules, which would also need to be stored in an airtight container. Pic 207 shows a capsule hand-filled with **lion's mane** mushroom powder instead of psilocybin, which explains the creamy color of the powder in this picture.

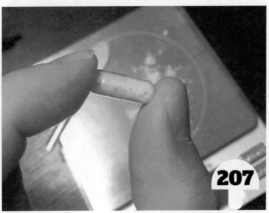

Blue Thumb   Sean McNamara

Pic 208 shows a bag of empty capsules which you can order online. These are Size 2 capsules, which can hold at least 0.06 grams of psilocybin mushroom powder. Size 2 is a relatively small capsule, great for people who have trouble swallowing large capsules.

You can buy kits online to hand-fill capsules individually, or to fill dozens of capsules at the same time using special trays. It's important for me to maintain precise doses. So, when using capsules, I fill them individually, weighing each one for accuracy.

A Size 2 capsule weighs close to 0.05 grams. Therefore, I can weigh a filled capsule and do the basic math to determine if it contains too much or too little for my microdose, and then open it up and make the necessary adjustments to it. Then I weigh it again to make sure it's the right amount.

Pics 209, 210, and 211 show one of the tools that comes with a capsule-filling kit I purchased online. Lion's mane mushroom powder is used in these examples.

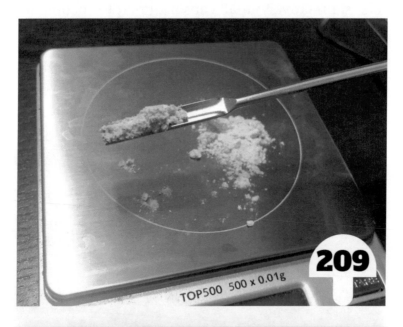

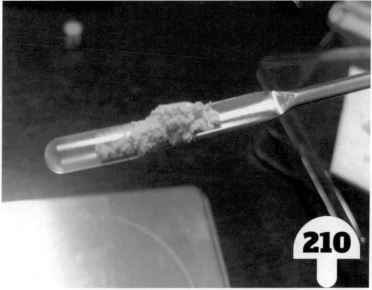

Pic 211 shows me coaxing the powder into the capsule.

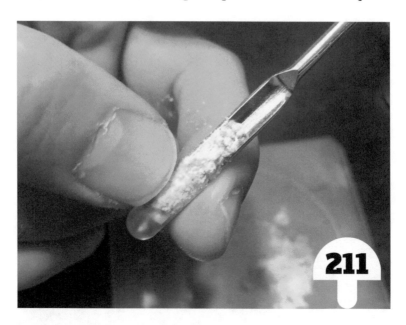

Voice of Experience: Hand filling individual capsules for precise dosages **is a major time-suck**. It takes me several minutes to accurately fill and weigh a single capsule.

That's why, after a couple of filling sessions, I stopped using capsules altogether.

The only reason I would ever use capsules is if I was staying overnight away from home and needed to take one or two micro doses with me.

Pics 213, 214 and 215 on pgs. 184 to 187 show how I take my microdose, which is quicker and easier than filling a capsule.

Consuming Your Mushrooms

I always weigh my dosage before adding it to food or beverages (Pic 212). Precision is an essential aspect of responsible use.

My favorite way to take my microdose is to dump it straight from the scale into my morning oatmeal (Pic 213).

Pic 214. Can you see the psilocybin in my oats? I'll thoroughly mix it in before eating them, though.

Another way I take my microdose is by adding it to tea (Pic 215). For example, I sometimes drink Turkey Tail mushroom tea, and add in Lion's Mane powder along with the psilocybin.

There are always floaters in the tea, but I don't mind them, and I wipe up the remainders from the edge of the cup with my finger and eat them for maximum benefit.

Part Five Equipment List

You will decide for yourself which of the following items you need based on which technique you choose to do after carefully reading the step-by-step instructions in this section.

These are in addition to items already mentioned in earlier lists which you may need here.

- vegetable dehydrator

- sealable sandwich bags

- sealable plastic containers

- amber-colored glass containers

- coffee or herb grinder

- fillable capsules

- capsule-filling kit/tools (available online)

- electric kitchen scale that can measure to 0.01 grams

PART SIX:

CONTINUING THE CYCLE

Multiply Your Own Supply

Let's assume you've spent a couple of months growing your mushrooms, harvesting, and storing them. Once you've consumed them all, what are you going to do?

- Option #1 Buy someone else's spores the way you did the first time by ordering a spore syringe online.
- Option #2 Use your own spores, for free.

By planning ahead, you can supply yourself with everything you need for future grows. If you possess dry mushroom spores in the form of spore prints, there are a variety of ways to turn them into mycelium for colonizing either PF Tek jars or grain spawn for use in bulk substrate.

This section will show you different methods of using your own spores, and also using live mushroom tissue, which is a process called *cloning*:

- Inoculating agar plates with spores
- Inoculating agar plates with tissue (cloning)
- Inoculating liquid culture with colonized agar
- Inoculating jars of substrate with agar
- Inoculating jars of substrate with colonized liquid culture
- Multiplying your agar to other agar plates
- Reusing a spent spore syringe to fill it again

The first step to multiplying your own supply is collecting spore prints.

Part Six: Continuing the Cycle

Collecting Spore Prints

Spores are collected when the caps are mature and the veil covering their gills underneath have torn away. The process is simple. Carefully cut the cap off the stipe, then place it on tinfoil overnight, during which time the cap will drop the millions of miniscule spores stored inside it. More details follow on the following pages.

As you can see in Pic 216, the veils have torn away beneath the caps. They appear slightly darkened, indicating spores have already begun to drop. This is a great time to cut the caps and begin collecting.

Blue Thumb   Sean McNamara

_____Harvest the whole mushrooms with the caps that appear ready to drop spores, or which have already begun doing so (Pic 217). Then, carefully cut the caps off.

You can tell they're ready to drop spores because their gills are darkened by spores (Pic 218).

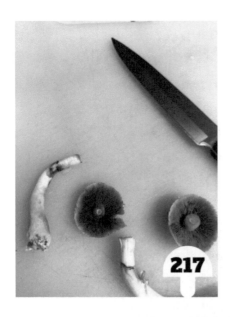

Part Six: Continuing the Cycle

_____Place the caps face-down on large pieces of tinfoil. Avoid them touching each other. You want the spores to land on the foil, not on another mushroom.

_____Place a jar or glass over each cluster of mushroom caps and insert a toothpick or other clean object just beneath the rim (Pic 29). This is to prevent humidity build-up.

However, spores are designed to float through the air. So, make sure your spore collection area is in a room free of wind or significant air movement.

You want the spores to drop straight down onto the foil, and remain there.

_____Allow the caps to remain beneath the glass for at least 24 hours.

_____Carefully remove each cap using a fork or even the toothpick you used to tilt the edge of the glass (Pics 220 and 221). Be careful not to smear the spore print by accidentally squashing the cap when trying to lift it up.

Part Six: Continuing the Cycle

_____Carefully look at the center of the spore print in Pic 222. Do you see the moisture droplets? This spore should **not** be stored until it is completely dry, as in Pic 223.

Blue Thumb   Sean McNamara

Pic 224 is an example of where the spore prints should be positioned on the tinfoil.

_____Fold the tinfoil in such a way as to seal the edges (Pic 225).

_____You may choose to write the date you collected the spores, and what strain they were. In Pic 226, "Ec" is shorthand for Ecuadorian.

_____Store your spore prints inside an air-tight container, and don't forget to add a couple desiccant packets for extra protection against humidity (Pic 227). If stored properly, your spores can remain dormant and ready for use for years to come. If the laws change in the future making it impossible to purchase spores online, you'll be glad you stored your own supply.

Preparing Agar Plates at Home

Agar plates are plastic or glass containers which hold a nutritious gel made of *agar*. Agar comes from algae. However, these plates can also be filled with gel made from other ingredients, such as *PDA*, potato dextrose agar.

The internet Is filled with various recipes you can use to fill your agar plates.

In this guide, you're shown how to prepare empty plastic agar plates using one easy recipe.

Did I purchase empty agar plates when I started doing this? No. I visited my local mycology supply store and purchased pre-poured agar plates.

After I grew mycelium and used it up, I was left with a full set of plates ready to be filled with fresh agar.

This is just a long way of telling you that **if you don't want to make your own agar plates, and want to buy them pre-filled instead, that's alright. You can skip this section** and look ahead in this guide to learn how to use your pre-filled plates.

Perhaps after you've used them, you'll keep the empty plates and learn how to fill them on your own at that time, the same way I did.

Pic 228 shows empty plastic agar plates.

Filling your agar plates is the last phase of two seaparate tasks. One task is to sterilize your plates. The other task is to prepare the hot, liquid agar for pouring into the plates.

For simplicity, you'll first learn how to sterilize the plates and prepare them for pouring. But be aware this step should be done while the liquid agar is cooling down from its sterilization process.

You'll learn how to do both tasks, one at a time, but **in the real world you'll be doing aspects of both tasks at the same time.**

Sterilizing Agar Plates

_____Put on your facemask.

_____Wash the plates with soap and hot water and air-dry them.

_____Prepare your workspace, either your still air box or your flow hood by cleaning it with isopropyl alcohol (Pic 229). If using a flow hood, make sure the fan is running from the very beginning to maintain positive air pressure in the space.

Part Six: Continuing the Cycle

_____Inside your workspace, you'll set two bowls with their respective tongs.

The first bowl is a mixture of liquid bleach and water. The ratio for sterilization is **1 part bleach to 9 parts warm tap water**. The amount of total liquid you need will depend on the size of bowl you're using. You need enough to submerge at least one half of an agar plate (the base or lid).

The second bowl is filled with 70% or 90% isopropyl alcohol. Again, there should be enough to submerge at least one half of an agar plate.

If you are using a small flow hood, you won't be able to fit both bowls inside, as in Pic 230. Since you will be dipping the plates into the diluted bleach first, then into the alcohol, the bleach can be furthest away from the air filter, even just outside the flow hood.

But the bowl of alcohol should be inside the protected air space of the flow hood.

Blue Thumb   Sean McNamara

_____Using tongs, dunk the first side of one of your agar plates into the bowl of diluted bleach (Pic 231). Let it remain submerged for **two minutes**.

_____Then, using the same tongs, pick up the plate and drop it into the bowl of alcohol. Submerge the plate for **30 seconds,** then pull it out with the other set of tongs and set it inside your workspace (flow hood or still air box) to dry.

Part Six: Continuing the Cycle

Pic 232 shows sterilized plates drying while a jar filled with hot liquid agar is introduced to the workspace. Before it was introduced, the jar was wiped down with isopropyl alcohol.

At this point, you'll continue by learning how to fill the plates with agar. **Later, you'll learn how to make and sterilize the agar itself.**

Pouring Agar Onto Plates

Note: You'll also want to read the next chapter *About Condensation and Pouring Temperatures* before pouring your plates.

_____Remove the foil from the jar of hot agar (Pic 233).

_____Pour just enough agar onto each plate to cover the bottom. Replace the cover of each plate as quickly as possible, stacking them inside your workspace (Pics 234 and 235).

_____If using a flow hood, keep the fan running while you **leave the filled agar plates inside to cool overnight.** If using a still air box, leave the plates inside and use paper or plastic to seal the arm holes.

_____Once they've cooled off, use either *parafilm* (Pic 236), which you can order online, or plastic food wrap (Pic 237) to seal the plates.

If you choose to use plastic food wrap, be sure to purchase a brand made from **polyvinyl (PVC). This material is *gas permeable*.** This provides the same benefits (gas exchange) the micropore tape did for the jars you used for colonizing substrate.

A quick online query will tell you if the brand of plastic wrap in your cupboard is made from gas permeable polyvinyl or not.

If it's your **first time using parafilm**, you may be surprised to find that although it's rolled like masking tape, it's not adhesive like tape. To use it, cut a piece from the roll long enough to completely wrap around the circumference of the plate.

While pressing one end of the parafilm strip against the rim of the plate, stretch the length of the tape, pulling it along the rim so it naturally curves and tightens around the edges. Then smooth it out with your fingers. The tension from being stretched will cause it to adhere (Pic 238).

Part Six: Continuing the Cycle

_____Use a marker and write the date when you removed the plates from your workspace (Pic 239). Store them someplace dark, away from extreme temperatures.

Do not put them in the refrigerator *yet*.

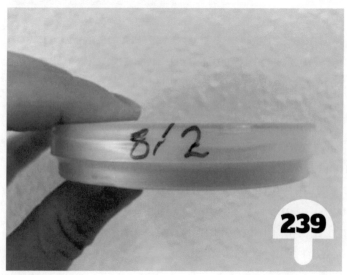

Blue Thumb   Sean McNamara

Even though you were careful while sterilizing your empty agar plates, and when pouring the liquid agar into them, it's possible that mold, bacteria, or other germs landed inside the plate before you protected it with parafilm or plastic food wrap.

The only way to know if your plates are clean and free of unwanted germs is to let them sit for a week at room temperature. If any germs landed in a plate, it'll be obvious by the end of that week. **You do *not* want to unknowingly introduce your spores to a plate infected with competing organisms.**

That's why you <u>don't </u>want to store your filled plates in the refrigerator immediately after they cool down. The cold temperature will slow down the growth of any unwanted organisms, fooling you into thinking your plates are clean.

Once your **clean** plates are mostly colonized with psilocybin mycelium, which can take several weeks, **then** you can put them in the fridge for long-term storage. Placing them in the fridge <u>upside-down</u> prevents any new condensation from dripping onto the growing mycelium.

Pic 240 shows an infected plate 5 days after being poured. Good thing I didn't waste my spores on it!

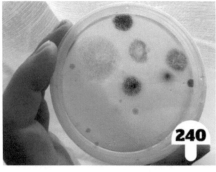

Pics 241 and 242 show a plate of Lion's Mane mushroom mycelium (the white matter) infected by bacteria or mold (the dark green spots).

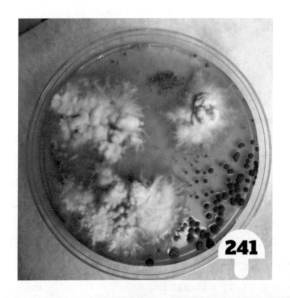

If you've been resistant to wearing a facemask when using your clean workspace, perhaps this will change your mind.

Just for fun, open one of your agar plates after it has cooled off completely, cough on it several times, then close it.

Set it somewhere apart from the clean plates and check on it one week later.

Whatever you see growing on the plate probably inhabits your mouth all the time. If you have a healthy immune system and maintain your personal hygiene, it's probably not a problem for you.

About Condensation and Pouring Temps

At best, excess condensation inside your agar plate will merely stain the solidified agar. At worst, it will ruin it or contribute to infection by unwanted organisms.

A little bit of condensation is almost unavoidable, and the only problem it causes is difficulty looking through the lid to see what's growing on the solidified agar.

Condensation is caused by the difference in temperature between the hot liquid agar and the surrounding air. The hotter the agar is when being poured, the more water vapor it releases, which is then trapped inside the plate, condensing into water droplets.

Therefore, keeping an electronic thermometer nearby is essential to pouring the agar at the right temperature.

I did an experiment with liquid agar prepared in a pot. It was not intended for real use, so I didn't use sterile procedures. My goal was to find the ideal temperature for minimizing condensation.

Pic 243 shows agar at 122.7°F (50.4°C), and Pic 244 shows agar at 117.1°F (47.3°C).

Pic 245 shows the two plates soon after being poured. The one on the left was poured hotter, at 122.7°F. The one on the right was poured cooler, at 117.1°F.

Compare their levels of condensation.

Blue Thumb   Sean McNamara

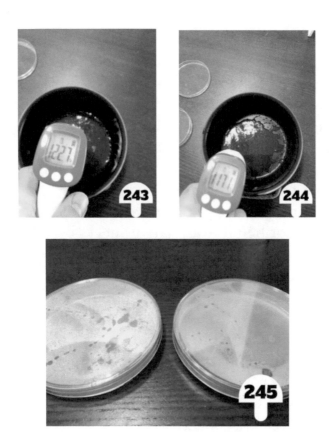

Pic 246 shows the same two plates the following day. You'll notice the condensation has naturally evaporated to a large degree by simply being left at room temperature inside their sterile workspaces.

Voice of Experience: Pouring agar is an act of finesse and takes some practice. Hot liquid agar cools rapidly, several degrees per minute. You should take its temperature frequently until it approaches 122°F, and then begin pouring rapidly, filling one plate, replacing the lid, then pouring the next one. If you move too slowly, the agar will cool to a point where it hardens and stops pouring from the jar.

Many growers prefer to sterilize their liquid agar in used liquor bottles with narrow necks because the agar cools down slower than it does with a wide mouth jar. It's also more difficult for unwanted organisms to enter a liquor bottle than a jar's mouth.

If you decide to use this type of bottle, **do <u>not</u> plug it closed with its original cork or cap** (because of the pressure buildup inside the cooker).

Simply cover the bottle's mouth with tinfoil, the same way you would cover a jar's lid when putting it inside the pressure cooker.

If you want to use a cap to keep the liquid in the bottle from cooling too quickly when you begin pouring it, pierce the cap with a thick nail and stick a micropore disk or tape (Pic 10, pg. 29) over the hole. Then, cover it with tinfoil to keep water from dripping into it during the sterilization process.

The plates should be uncovered only long enough, and only partially, if possible, to pour the agar. Replace the plate lids as quickly as possible.

Making Agar

This chapter introduces just one of many possible recipes for making agar. The amounts shown below are enough to fill at least **8 agar plates**.

INGREDIENTS FOR AGAR

Any of the following which are not available in your grocery store can be ordered online.

- 5 grams agar powder (Pic 247)
- 5 grams light malt powder extract (Pic 248)
- 0.5 grams nutritional yeast (Pic 249)
- 250 ml hot water

248

249

Blue Thumb   Sean McNamara

_____ Combine the dry ingredients, the pour them into a small pot filled with 250 ml of hot water (Pic 250).

_____Stir to dissolve the chunks (Pic 251).

_____Pour the mixture into canning jar with the same lid you used for inoculating substrate, with micropore tape and injection port (Pic 252).

_____Cover it in foil, put it in the pressure cooker, and add a couple inches of water just like when you sterilized the jars of substrate. Keep in mind you'll be sterilizing it for only 45 minutes instead of 90.

_____Lock the lid closed all the way, then turn the heat to high.

_____When the gauge says you've reached 15 PSI (the rocker will start rocking and being noisy) lower the heat to medium-high. It usually takes around 20-25 minutes to build up to 15 PSI.

_____Once the cooker has reached 15 PSI, set a timer for **45 minutes.**

_____At **45 minutes**, turn OFF the heat and let the pressure cooker sit exactly where it is on your stove **for several hours, without opening the lid**. It will be very hot and pressurized until then – don't touch it!

This cooling stage is a great time to sterilize your empty agar plates and leave them in your workspace to **dry in a sterile environment.**

The plates may be perfectly dry long before the pressure cooker has de-pressurized enough to open it. That's alright. If you are using a homemade flow hood, continue blowing clean air over the agar plates without interruption.

To increase the positive air pressure, you might lean the container's lid against the opening to partially block the air flow. This will make it even more difficult for germs to waft into the workspace.

If you're using a still air box, there's nothing more to do but let them sit inside with the arm holes blocked off to keep bad air out.

Once the pressure gauge reads "0" and the exterior is cool enough to touch, open the pressure cooker to retrieve the jar of hot liquid agar. Take care not to burn your hand or fingers when lifting the jar out of the pressure cooker, it will still be quite hot inside.

That brings you to what was happening on pg. 203, Pic 233 in the chapter *Pouring Agar Onto Plates*.

Spores to Agar

Let's assume you have several agar plates that you poured yourself or purchased a week ago, and they're still *clean*, meaning that no unwanted organisms have begun growing on the agar.

Therefore, you've got a potential home for your collected spores to move into and become mycelium.

Spore cells are intelligent enough to come out of dormancy when they detect ideal conditions for growth. When you smear spores onto agar, they know they've hit a nutritious jackpot.

Over several days, you'll notice the dark smear on your agar fading away. Not to worry, though. The spores are simply transitioning into mycelium, which is almost invisible at first. A week later, you'll notice a fine, white network of mycelial strands beginning to spread across the plate.

Several weeks later, your agar will be completely covered by a white carpet of mycelium ready for use in substrate, grain spawn, liquid culture, or even for transfer to other agar plates. **At that point, you can refrigerate your plates to slow the growth and preserve the mycelium for future use.**

Imagine taking a fully colonized agar plate and slicing it into twelve pieces (in a clean workspace, of course) and transferring each piece into one of twelve fresh agar plates. Then a few weeks later, you repeat the process. Over several months, a single plate has multiplied into 144 plates!

Of course, you don't need that many for your personal use. This example simply illustrates the versatility and multiplicability of working with agar.

_____Put on your facemask and clean yourself before using your workspace for agar work.

_____After wiping down the outside of the tinfoil packet with alcohol, introduce the enclosed spore print to your workspace. You'll open the packet just before you're ready to scrape it onto your agar plate (Pic 253).

_____Do the same for your agar plate, wiping it down and then unwrapping in only after putting it inside your workspace.

Part Six: Continuing the Cycle

_____You could use either a knife, scalpel, a "loop" (typically used in laboratories) or even a metal spoon or fork to scrape a portion of a spore print onto a clean agar plate (Pic 254, next page). No matter which tool you use, you should sterilize it. There are at least two ways to sterilize your tool.

Tool sterilization technique #1

Step 1. Wash it with soap and water and air-dry.

Step 2. Wipe it down with isopropyl alcohol.

Step 3. Put it inside a canning jar with a hole and micropore tape on it. If the jar is too small, use a large mason jar, also with a hole in the lid with micropore tape on it (Pic 6, pg. 27). With either type of jar, cover the lid with tinfoil.

Step 4. Pressure cook the jar for 45 minutes at 15 PSI

Step 5. After it has cooled down sufficiently (several hours later), take the jar out of the pressure cooker, leaving the tinfoil on. Immediately introduce it into your clean workspace but wipe the jar down with isopropyl alcohol just before you do.

Tool sterilization technique #2

_____Use the same technique you used for sterilizing your empty agar plates, shown on pg. 199.

Remember to use an agar plate that has sat at room temperature for at least a week without showing any signs of contamination.

Pic 254 shows a sterilized spoon being used to scrape a portion of spores onto an opened agar plate.

Pic 255 shows chunks of spores landed onto the plate.

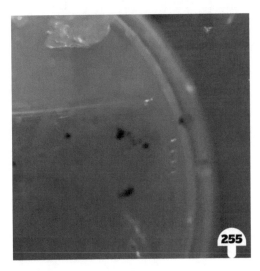

_____Close the agar plate as quickly as possible, then seal it with fresh parafilm or polyvinyl plastic food wrap.

_____Store the plate someplace dark and away from extreme temperatures for several weeks until the plate is significantly colonized.

Pic 256 shows the same plate several days later. Notice the faint mycelium spreading out from the spores.

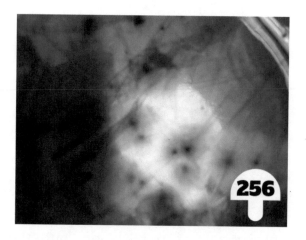

Pic 257 shows a plate poured with PDA (potato dextrose agar). In this case, I **smeared** the spores into the gel using a sterilized knife.

Pic 258 shows a smeared PDA plate **4 days after** inoculation with spores. The smear is fading out as the spores transform into the faint, white wisps of young mycelium.

Pic 259 shows the same plate **two weeks later.**

Pic 260 shows a well colonized plate with chunks taken out for inoculating jars of substrate and jars of liquid culture. Agar is wonderfully versatile.

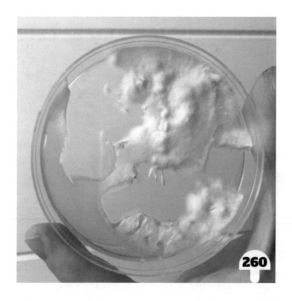

Pic 261 shows a closeup of the mycelium on the plate.

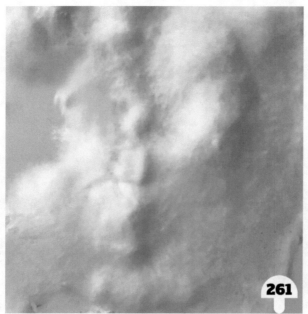

Blue Thumb   Sean McNamara

Cloning with Agar

There's another way to grow mycelium on agar plates. Instead of smearing spores, you can use a small piece of living mushroom tissue. This is called *cloning*, and it is so easy you might prefer it to using spores.

But remember the advantage of collecting spores is they stay viable in their dormant state for months, if not years.

With cloning, you must use a freshly harvested mushroom.

As with all other agar work, you'll use your clean workspace (flow hood or still air box).

_____Put on your facemask and clean yourself before using your workspace for agar work.

Pic 262 shows a freshly harvest mushroom from which the tissue sample will be taken.

Part Six: Continuing the Cycle

_____Split the mushroom open to access the unpolluted interior. Using a sterilized knife or scalpel to cut out a small piece of tissue (Pic 263).

_____Simply drop the tissue onto an agar plate and seal it as quickly as possible (Pic 264). Then leave it somewhere dark, away from extreme temperatures for several weeks.

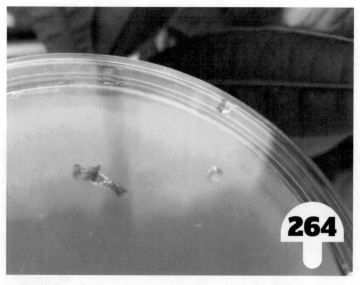

Blue Thumb   Sean McNamara

Pic 265 shows the mycelial growth **5 days after** inoculating the plate with live tissue.

Pics 266 shows the same tissue **two weeks after inoculation.**

Pic 267 is a closeup of Pic 266.

Making Liquid Culture with Agar

Imagine that instead of growing mycelium on a hard medium like agar, you grow it in a liquid like the way kombucha is grown. With kombucha, acetic acid bacteria and yeast work together in a nutrient rich liquid to provide you with nutritious probiotics.

With mushroom liquid culture, mycelium is introduced into a nutritious liquid medium to help it grow and produce even more mycelium.

In the technique below, you will inoculate your liquid medium with a small piece of colonized agar. But first, you must prepare the liquid medium.

PREPARING THE LIQUID CULTURE MEDIUM

Recipe and Extras for Liquid Culture Medium

- 1 gram of light malt powder extract

- 600 ml tap water (some growers prefer non-chlorinated, distilled water)

- 1 tall mason jar with modified lid (injection port and micropore tape)

- 2 one-inch glass marbles (Pic 268, next page)

_____Heat the water in a pot, then add the light malt extract powder, stirring until it is completely dissolved.

_____Drop the two marbles into the mason jar.

_____Pour all the dissolved malt extract into the mason jar.

_____Close the lid, and cover it with tinfoil

_____Pressure cook the mason jar at 15 PSI **for only 25 minutes.** Any longer and it could thicken. Slight darkening is natural and nothing to be worried about.

Blue Thumb   Sean McNamara

Pic 269 shows a fresh jar of liquid culture media with marbles at the bottom, ready for the pressure cooker (it just needs the tinfoil over the lid).

INOCULATING THE STERILIZED LIQUID CULTURE MEDIUM

_____Put on your facemask and clean yourself before using your workspace for agar and liquid culture work.

_____Prepare your clean workspace as usual.

_____Introduce the sterilized, room-temp mason jar into the workspace after wiping it down with alcohol.

_____Introduce a colonized agar plate after wiping it down with alcohol.

_____Introduce a sterilized cutting tool such as a knife or scalpel. **Voice of Experience:** I've also used a sterilized spoon.

_____Remove the tinfoil from the mason jar but set it aside inside your workspace face-down so it remains clean. You'll use it later.

_____Unscrew the mason jar's lid so you can quickly open it after you've cut a small piece of colonized agar from its plate.

_____Open the agar plate and cut out a small piece of agar. Immediately replace the plate's lid, then open the mason jar and drop the piece of colonized agar into it.

_____Close the lid, and replace the tinfoil, cover the lid.

_____Put tape on the jar and write the date on it.

_____Place the jar someplace dark and away from extreme temperatures. Over several weeks, the mycelium on the piece of agar will expand, forming a thick cloud of tissue inside the liquid. This is the *culture*.

_____It's important to disperse the culture for ease of use later. To do this, gently but swiftly swirl the marbles around the bottom of the jar to create turbulence. This will break up the floating mycelium. Do this once or twice each day. Don't splash any liquid up toward the micropore tape. It should always be dry.

Pic 270 shows a piece of colonized agar floating inside a recently sterilized mason jar of liquid culture media.

Pic 271 shows the jar several weeks later. The agar has been fully consumed, and the mycelium has become the floating culture.

_____After several weeks of growth, the jar can be stored in the refrigerator to slow down growth, for future use. The liquid culture can stay viable for a couple of months, if not longer.

Inoculating Jars with Agar

Inoculating jars with agar is easy to do. One advantage to this is it skips the process of spores transforming into mycelium. Since the agar is colonized with mycelium, you speed up the process of colonizing the substrate in the jar.

The added nutritional supply from the unconsumed agar also helps the mycelium propagate quickly.

You can use this technique for jars filled with brown rice flour and vermiculite for PF Tek, or with corn or other types of grain spawn for use with bulk substrate.

_____Put on your facemask and clean yourself before using your workspace for agar and substrate work.

_____Prepare your clean workspace as usual.

_____Introduce the sterilized jar of substrate (or grain/corn) into the workspace after wiping it down with alcohol.

_____Introduce a colonized agar plate after wiping it down with alcohol.

_____Introduce a sterilized cutting tool such as a knife or scalpel. Again, I've also used a sterilized spoon.

_____Unscrew the jar's lid so you can quickly open it after you've cut a small piece of colonized agar from its plate.

_____Open the agar plate and cut out a small piece of agar. Immediately replace the plate's lid, then open the jar and drop the piece of colonized agar into it. **Try to make the agar land face-down so the mycelium on its surface makes direct contact with the substrate.**

But if it lands the other way, that's okay, the mycelium will just need 235a little more time to spread into the substrate.

_____Close the lid, then put tape on the jar and write the date on it.

_____Place the jar someplace dark and away from extreme temperatures. Over several weeks, the mycelium on the piece of agar will colonize the substrate.

Pic 272 shows a jar inoculated with agar and partially colonized with mycelium. Note the chunk of agar is still visible on the surface. It will shrink as it's consumed over time.

Inoculating Jars with Liquid Culture

In the previous chapter, you learned the advantage of using agar to inoculate jars is it skips the step of waiting for spores to transform into mycelium. Inoculating jars with liquid culture offers the exact same advantage.

However, **using liquid culture requires the use of a syringe.** You can purchase a brand-new syringe from an online retailer or your local mycology supply store.

Or you could sterilize your original (but empty) spore syringe. **Instructions for sterilizing your used spore syringe are in the next chapter, *Reusing Spore Syringes*.**

_____Put on your facemask and clean yourself before using your workspace for liquid culture work.

_____Prepare your clean workspace as usual.

_____Introduce the mason jar of liquid culture into the workspace after wiping it down with isopropyl alcohol. Keep the tinfoil over the lid.

_____Introduce a jar of substrate after wiping it down with isopropyl alcohol.

_____Introduce an empty and sterilized syringe after wiping it down with isopropyl alcohol.

_____Remove the tinfoil and pierce the injection port with the syringe. Since you'll be drawing liquid culture from the mason jar, the syringe should be plunged all the way before injecting it into the jar.

_____Tilt the jar so the tip of the needle contacts a nice, thick section of the floating culture, and pull back the plunger to completely fill the syringe with mycelium (Pic 273).

_____Inoculate as many jars as you wish by injecting 1 to 1.5 cc's of liquid culture the same way you did with your original spore syringe.

Imagine other ways of using liquid culture. For example, you could also inoculate fresh jars of liquid culture medium (1 cc each) or agar plates (just a few drops in each) with it.

Blue Thumb   Sean McNamara

Reusing Spore Syringes

After you use a spore syringe, it's possible to sterilize it for future use, such as for inoculating your liquid culture. There's also an easier method, although it poses a greater risk of contamination

THE RISKY TECHNIQUE

Imagine you've inoculated the last jar of substrate, completely emptying your spore syringe. It's still enclosed inside your clean workspace.

Planning ahead, you'll also have an empty, sterilized jar inside your workspace.

Since you've been using your syringe inside of a clean workspace, you can assume the needle is still germ-free.

_____Put the cap back on the needle.

_____Unscrew the capped needle from the body of the syringe.

_____Open the empty sterilized jar and put the needle and the body of the syringe inside, then close it.

_____Put a layer of tinfoil over the lid or wrap the whole jar in plastic food wrap for extra protection.

_____Store the jar in your fridge until you want to reuse it.

<u>Optional: Flaming the needle before storing it in the jar</u>

Some people worry the needle can contract unwanted organisms while colonizing jars of substrate. I discuss this concern later, in the chapter *Should I Flame the Syringe Needle for Sterility?*

For now, you might choose to use a lighter and hold a flame to the needle for several seconds to kill any pathogens that may have landed on it.

Wait until the needle has cooled off before putting its plastic cap over it. Then unscrew the needle from the syringe body and put them inside the jar.

THE CONVENTIONAL TECHNIQUE

You will need the following:

- A small bowl of 1 part liquid bleach and 9 parts of water (just enough fluid to fill the syringe three times, 30 cc's)
- A small bowl of isopropyl alcohol, also enough to fill the syringe three times
- A small bowl of sterilized water which has cooled down slightly
- A mason jar with a hole and micropore tape in the lid
- A large, empty bowl for receiving 90 cc's of liquid squirted from the syringe

_____Put on your facemask and clean yourself before using your workspace for sterilizing your syringe.

_____Do the following 3 times: Draw 10 cc's of the bleach solution into the syringe, then squirt it out into the empty bowl.

_____Do the following 3 times: Draw 10 cc's of the isopropyl alcohol into the syringe, then squirt it out into the same bowl you used for the spent bleach solution.

_____Do the following 3 times: Draw 10 cc's of sterile water into the syringe, then then squirt it out into the same bowl you used for the spent bleach solution.

_____Cap the needle and unscrew it from the body of the syringe.

_____Wipe down the needle's cap and the body of the syringe with isopropyl alcohol and place them inside the empty mason jar.

_____Pressure cook the jar with the syringe and needle inside for **45 minutes at 15 PSI. Be sure to add three or four inches of water into the pressure cooker as usual** before closing the lid and turning on the heat.

Part Six: Continuing the Cycle

_____After the cooker has cooled off and depressurized, put the jar in your refrigerator for future use.

Pic 274 shows two needles and their syringe bodies inside the mason jar with tinfoil on the lid, ready for pressure cooking.

Filling Your Own Spore Syringe

Along with reusing your old spore syringe for liquid culture inoculation as explained in the last two chapters, you can also fill it with spore prints you've taken from your own mushroom caps.

Like the other techniques you've learned so far, making your own spore syringe requires sterilization and either a flow hood or still air box. Since the spore syringe is the beginning of an entire cycle of mushroom cultivation, it's more important than ever to keep everything as clean as possible.

First, the syringe itself should already be sterilized using the instructions in the previous chapter. Or you can purchase an empty syringe which will arrive sterilized inside its package (but check with the vendor to make sure this is the case).

Second, you'll sterilize the water which will be used to suspend the spores inside the syringe.

Third, you'll use that water to rinse the spores off the tinfoil and into the water's own container.

Fourth, you'll draw all the water with the spores in it into the syringe, then cap the needle and store the syringe inside the sterilized jar.

**Please note, since you've learned how to use your pressure cooker by now from previous techniques, I won't repeat the same details I have in earlier chapters. Just remember to add a few inches of water before locking it closed and turning on the heat.

***And don't forget to wipe down anything you introduce into your workspace with isopropyl alcohol.

STERILIZING THE SYRINGE WATER

You'll need the items in Pic 275:

- One 16-ounce canning jar with micropore tape on the lid.
- One 8-ounce canning jar (no lid needed)
- tinfoil

_____Fill the 8-ounce jar with 10 cc's of **distilled water**.

     We're not worried about germs in the water since they'll be eliminated in the pressure cooker, along with germs lingering on the surface of the bowl or glass. But we are concerned with chlorine and other chemicals, hence the distilled water.

_____Place the filled 8-ounce jar inside the empty 16-ounce jar (Pic 276).

Pic 276 shows the jar-within-a-jar, with water inside the small jar.

_____Close the lid on the 16-ounce jar and cover with tinfoil.

_____Pressure cook the jar at 15 PSI for 45 minutes.

_____Put on your facemask and clean yourself before using your workspace to fill your sterilized syringe with spores.

_____After everything has cooled down to room temperature, usually by the next morning, introduce the "**jar within a jar**" into your clean workspace.

_____Introduce the jar containing your **sterilized syringe** inside your workspace.

_____Introduce a **spore print** enclosed in tinfoil into your workspace.

_____Open the 16-ounce jar and pull out the smaller one.

_____Pull the syringe out of its jar, connect the needle, and uncap it only when you're ready to do the next step. Keep it capped anytime you're not using it for sterility.

_____Draw the water from the jar into the syringe (Pic 278).

_____Open the spore print and hold it over the jar without it touching the glass. To take the picture I had to lean the foil against the interior of the glass – but I would never risk contamination by doing that under real circumstances (Pic 279).

_____Forcefully squirt water from the syringe onto the spore print until all the spores have dribbled into the glass.

I know, I know! In Pic 280, the stream of water doesn't look very forceful, but I was doing this while holding the camera ☺ You really want to give it a strong squirt.

_____It will take multiple squirts to break down the spores and fill the jar with them (Pic 281). Continue by refilling the syringe with the same water from the jar. Each time, you may notice it holding more tiny dark spots.

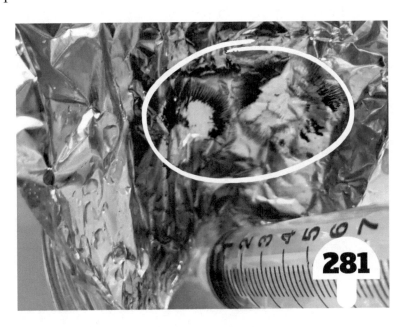

Eventually, all the spores will be washed into the jar (Pic 282).

_____When all the spores have been washed off the foil, draw all the spore-laden water into the syringe and put the cap on. You now have your very own homemade syringe (Pic 283).

The dark spots you see are clumps of many cells. There are millions of spores inside this syringe.

Now, nature's cycle can repeat itself under your care, for as long as you want.

Congratulations!

Part Six Equipment List

You will decide for yourself which of the following items you need based on which technique you choose to do after carefully reading the step-by-step instructions in this section.

These are in addition to items already mentioned in earlier lists which you may need here.

- toothpicks

- plastic agar plates

- liquid bleach

- parafilm

- polyvinyl plastic food wrap

- empty liquor bottle with narrow neck

- agar powder

- light malt extract powder

- nutritional yeast

- one-inch glass marbles (you can find them online)

- large mason jar

PART SEVEN:

ODDS AND ENDS

Spotting Mold

Stay on the lookout for mold especially in the fruiting stage.

If one of the cakes has something blue, green, orange, or that appears like a cobweb (this, in fact, is called *cobweb mold*) growing on it, take it out of the monotub and throw it away before the mold spreads to the other cakes. The same applies if you suspect mold in one of your jars of grain spawn (popcorn).

Pics 284 shows cobweb mold at the base of the cake.

Pic 285 is a closeup of cobweb mold.

Pic 286 shows green mold at the base of a different cake.

Pic 287 is a closeup of the green mold.

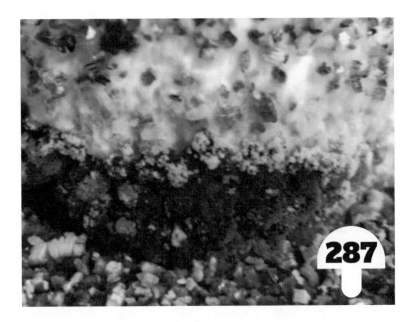

Mold can also grow on bulk substrate. But since I've only experienced mold on PF Tek cakes, and never on bulk substrate, I don't have any photos of that to share, thankfully. But mold is mold, so now you know how to spot it. If it's not white mycelium or the bluish hue of bruised mycelium, it's probably mold.

There are many recommendations about how to deal with a mold infestation aside from throwing out your substrate, such as simply cutting off the infected part or spraying it with 3% hydrogen peroxide.

I play it safe and dispose of infected substrate, getting it out of the environment as soon as possible so tiny mold spores don't begin floating in the air, possibly landing on other substrate.

Weird Growth

Whether due to environmental conditions or genetic anomalies, sometimes mushrooms look a little weird. But it doesn't mean they're bad.

For example, Pics 288 and 289 on the next page show a mushroom whose hollow has extended all the way through the cap.

I have read from various sources that a wide hollow canal in the stipe is the result of very hot growing conditions. The mushroom below grew during a time when our air conditioner died for a couple weeks, and daytime temperatures went as high as 84°F (28.9°C).

The temperature inside colonizing jars or tubs of substrate is typically warmer than the air outside because of thermogenesis. This is because process as mycelium consumes nutrition and grows, it produces heat.

This means the temperature inside the tub was probably even higher than 84°F. So, I'm not surprised the hollow line was extreme enough to expand through the cap. I'm pleasantly surprised the heat didn't pave the way for mold infestation.

Part Seven: Odds and Ends

Pic 290 shows another oddity. A cap with a strange protuberance on it. Perhaps also the result of abnormally hot growing conditions?

Do you remember when I incubated harvested substrate for three days in the dark and then returned it to fruiting conditions for a second flush? Remember those ghostly gray pins that grew in the dark? You can see one in the background in Pic 290. Remarkably, a new pin grew as a perfectly healthy extension of one of the old pins when fruiting conditions returned (Pic 291).

Blue Thumb   Sean McNamara

Pic 292 is a closeup of that pin, taken while cleaning the harvested second flush.

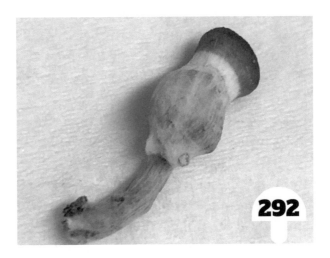

First-time growers may be concerned at seeing thick, fuzzy texture at the base of some of their mushrooms, fearing mold. **Don't worry, it's just mycelium** (Pic 293).

Growing in Pots, Yes You Can!

At one point, I asked myself "Do we really need these monotubs and jars to grow mushrooms? Can't we create a more natural environment for them?" That gave me the idea to attempt growing mushrooms in pots, just like plants.

Also, I had 4 jars of grain spawn (corn) which had taken forever to colonize, and I didn't know what to do with them since I already had some substrate incubating in my closet for my next grow. In fact, the jars weren't even finished colonizing, but I'd lost my patience and thought I'd use them anyway.

For this experiment, I used some old planters I found hidden away. Three of them had plastic liners for draining. The fourth was a low, wide clay pot with holes in the bottom. It was set inside a separate clay platter.

Here is the order of events:

**Note: <u>None</u> of the tasks in my potting experiment were done in a clean workspace. I really wanted to test the limits.

All the preparation was done in my kitchen, which is usually one of the most germ-infested areas of anyone's home.

First, I decided to combine equal part coco coir, vermiculite, and potting soil. I loosely estimated the amounts needed to fill four small pots when combined with the colonized corn kernels. I began by mixing the coco coir and vermiculite with some tap water in a large bowl (Pic 294, next page).

Then, I combined the mix with regular potting soil (Pic 295). I made sure to test the whole mix for *field capacity* by squeezing a handful to make sure only a few drops of water escaped my clenched fist.

I also sprinkled the combination with a spoonful of gypsum for added nutrition, then mixed it in by hand (Pic 296).

Since some of the corn from the grain spawn wasn't colonized yet, I crumbled it off the rest of the cakes after birthing from their jars (Pic 297).

I hand-mixed the ingredients together to evenly distribute the crumbled and colonized corn (Pic 298). Then I filled each pot with a portion of the mix (Pic 299).

I wasn't sure how to proceed at that point. So, I selected two of the pots with plastic liners to be wrapped with PVC food wrap, secured with a rubber band (Pic 300). I decided to incubate these two pots in a dark closet for ten days.

The other pot with a liner and the clay pot with its own platter were placed on a table near north-facing windows for ambient light, completely uncovered. Pic 301 shows the clay pot at that time.

Living in Colorado, where the air is exceptionally dry, I knew I had to pay special attention to the soil's moisture in the uncovered pots. I focused on two activities.

Every other day, I took the pots to my kitchen sink and soaked them from underneath. After several minutes, I drained the excess water and returned the pots to their spots near the window.

Also, twice or three times a day I would notice the top layer of the soil would dry out, so I would spray it with just enough water to darken it with moisture.

Before the ten days of incubation for the two plastic-wrapped pots in my was complete, a very funky smell began to fill the closet. I took a close whiff of the surface of the plastic on both pots, and it was obvious the odor was emanating from only one of them. I moved the stinky pot outside and covered it with an upside-down pot to continue incubating it in darkness.

I left the other, non-smelly pot in the closet to finish its incubation there. Pic 302 represents how both the incubated pots looked after ten days, after taking their plastic wraps off. Note the mycelium on the surface. I placed the non-stinky pot on a bookcase to fruit.

302

Part Seven: Odds and Ends

The other two pots, the ones that did not go into incubation and were just placed uncovered near the window, never developed a white fluffy layer of mycelium on the surface like the incubated ones did. **But as you'll see, that wasn't a predictor of failure.**

Two weeks later, I awoke to find the first pins, which grew out of the clay pot (Pic 303).

I could tell they were happy by how fast they were growing. Pic 304 is taken only one day after Pic 303.

Meanwhile, recall that the stinky pot was left outside to fruit, while the non-stinky incubated pot was allowed to fruit atop my bookcase, also near the windows like the two other indoor pots.

Pic 305 is the mold that grew on the incubated pot allowed to fruit inside on my bookcase. Pic 306 is of the stinky pot that was kept outside. Uh oh! Green mold!

So, those two went into the garbage immediately. But the **clay pot** kept growing, until it was ready for harvesting and spore printing, **exactly 16 days from the day it was potted**, with **14 beautiful, healthy mushrooms growing from it!** See Pic 307.

As for the fourth pot, the one with the plastic liner but which had <u>not</u> been incubated and which was fruited alongside the clay pot, four little pins appeared on the same day the clay pot was harvested. It had slower growth, but at least it hadn't contracted mold like the other two with plastic liners.

I suspect those two contracted mold because I incubated them inside plastic wrap. My intention was to treat them the same way I treat bulk substrate in a monotub. But it turns out I created an ideal situation for mold growth.

One of the best deterrents against mold is simple fresh air, which clearly benefitted the mushrooms in the clay pot.

Does Mycelium Really Need Darkness?

As you've read in several techniques in this guide, I recommend incubating newly inoculated jars of substrate or monotubs of bulk substrate in the dark.

This might confuse some readers because many growers on online mushroom forums remark although a high carbon dioxide environment is indeed necessary for mycelium to spread, darkness is not.

Along with that, they say oxygen is what signals the mycelium to begin its fruiting stages, not the exposure to light.

Let me share an example which compels me to continue incubating in the dark.

When I've placed my newly inoculated jars in the closet, I lined them up in rows. The ones toward the back receive less of the accidental light that gets let in when I need to slide the closet door open to get something out of it.

Over the course of several weeks, I probably opened the closet door and allowed light to enter dozens of times. Most of the times I opened the door was to pull the jars out and inspect them one by one to check on their progress and spot any potential mold.

Over time, it became obvious that the jars kept further back in the closet had faster growing mycelium than the jars which were more exposed to more light over time.

I've seen this happen with multiple grows. **But I've also seen something that indicates the opposite effect of light.** I recently inoculated eight jars using the same spore syringe. In one of the jars, the mycelium colonized the substrate tremendously faster than those of the other seven jars. It was like *super* mycelium!

Eventually the other jars caught up, and it was time to fruit. I tried an experiment in which I made mini-monotubs, so that each cake had its own private space to fruit.

The tubs were all place equidistant from my north-facing glass doors to receive ambient light from outside. I also kept the overhead room light on during the day.

Even though all the cakes had been rolled in vermiculite, I noticed the super mycelium on the cake from the fast-growing jar had continued to thicken, growing through the vermiculite so much it seemed to cover it over entirely – but only on one side. Can you guess which side? It was the side that always faced the glass doors and received more light (Pic 308, next page).

The other side of the same cake, facing into the room that received most of its light from an overhead lamp, didn't grow the same way (Pic 309). That side grew just like all the other cakes did.

I don't believe it was a fluke that the exact half of the cake which faced significant natural light proliferated significantly faster than the dark side did.

However, I choose to continue to incubate my jars and monotubs in the dark. I'm sure they would still grow even with full exposure to light, but that's not an experiment I'm willing to spend time on.

But it leaves a question that you can answer yourself by incubating half of your jars in the dark, and half in the light. Science is fun!

Part Seven: Odds and Ends

Should I Flame the Syringe Needle for Sterility?

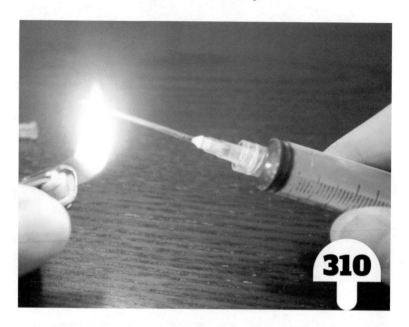

When I began cultivating mushrooms, I read in many sources that it's important to flame the syringe's needle (Pic 310) in between jars during inoculation. The notion is the needle could encounter mold or other germs when puncturing a jar's injection port. Or perhaps it could encounter airborne germs while waiting to inject the next jar in line.

For whatever reason, if it did contract any unwanted organisms, it could then transport those germs *inside* the next jar it inoculated.

That's why some growers recommend flaming the needle until it's red-hot, and then allowing it to cool for a few seconds before injecting it into the next jar. Some growers recommend also wiping the needle with a cotton ball or towel soaked in isopropyl alcohol.

Blue Thumb   Sean McNamara

I stopped flaming my needle and wiping it with alcohol during inoculations for several reasons.

Regarding wiping the needle with alcohol after it has been flamed – alcohol doesn't necessarily kill mold or other germs. So, touching the needle with a material like cotton or paper could do more harm than good. These could have germs on them that stick to the needle while it's being "cleaned."

One time, when I was inoculating a dozen jars, I decided to try an experiment. I flamed the needle before inoculating six of them, then labeled them so I could track their progress over the following weeks.

Obviously, I didn't flame the needle for the remaining six jars.

Aside from being curious about germs, I was also concerned that superheating the needle could heat the fluid inside the syringe too much.

Or perhaps even when I thought the needle had cooled down enough, the spores or liquid culture passing through it were being overheated and killed or neutralized before making it into the substrate.

Remember that failing to wait long enough for your substrate to cool down to room temperature (after being sterilized in the pressure cooker) could kill any spores or liquid culture you inoculate it with afterward.

There was also the logical consideration that during the time it took for the needle to cool down, it was being held aloft in the workspace for any passing airborne particles or germs to land on.

Wouldn't it be better to quickly move from one jar to the next, in-and-out so fast the needle spent more time inside the sterilized jars than outside in the air?

Part Seven: Odds and Ends

It turned out that a couple of the jars I inoculated with a flamed needle didn't produce any mycelium at all.

Another couple of those jars didn't show mycelial growth until a couple weeks *after* all the other jars began growing.

By contrast, all the jars I inoculated *without* flaming the needle grew mycelium at a regular pace, and without mold.

Therefore, I suspect flaming the needle reduced the number of bioactive spores released from the syringe immediately after flaming the needle.

At this point, some growers might respond with "You probably didn't wait long enough for the needle to cool down!" I would reply that by waiting around longer with the needle exposed to the air after flaming it sort of renders the exercise pointless.

To that, they would reply "But you're doing this inside a flow hood or still air box, so the air shouldn't be a problem." And finally, I say, "That's true! I am working in a clean air space. So why the need to flame the needle in the first place?"

By the way, if you still decide to use a lighter or some other fire starter in your workspace, don't do it while the fumes of recently wiped or sprayed isopropyl alcohol linger in the air.

Don't hold the flame too close to the walls or ceiling of your plastic flow hood or still air box. And for goodness sake, keep that bottle of isopropyl **alcohol** very far away when using **fire** in your workspace.

You just don't want to end up on the TV for doing something stupid. ☺

Blue Thumb   Sean McNamara

PART EIGHT:

RECORD KEEPING

Sample PF Tek
Tracking Sheet pg. 1

Event/Task	Date	Number of Days Since Previous Event (i.e., growing events)
Sterilize Jars	_____	____n/a____
Inoculate Jars	_____	____n/a____
First Appearance of Mycelium	_____	_____
Jars Half-Way Colonized	_____	_____
Jars Fully Colonized	_____	_____
Birthed and Dunked	_____	_____
Rolled and Put into Fruiting Conditions	_____	_____
First Pins Emerge	_____	_____
First Caps Develop	_____	_____
First Cap Tears its Veil	_____	_____
Harvest Day	_____	_____
Second Dunk (optional – for second flush)	_____	_____

Blue Thumb   Sean McNamara

Sample PF Tek
Tracking Sheet pg. 2

Return to Fruiting
Conditions
(second flush)   _____   _____

First Pins Emerge
(second flush)   _____   _____

First Caps Develop
(second flush)   _____   _____

First Cap Tears its
Veil
(second flush)   _____   _____

Harvest Day
(second flush)   _____   _____

Sample Bulk Substrate
Tracking Sheet Pg. 1

Event/Task	Date	Number of Days Since Previous Event (i.e., growing events)
Soak Corn (grain) for 24 Hours	_____	____n/a____
Boil, then Sterilize in Pressure Cooker	_____	____n/a____
Inoculate Jars of Sterilized Corn	_____	____n/a____
Jars Half-Way Colonized	_____	_____
Jars Fully Colonized	_____	_____
Prepare and Sterilize Bulk Substrate (coco coir and vermiculite) in Pressure Cooker	_____	_____
Combine Colonized Corn (grain spawn) with Bulk Substrate and Incubate for 10 days	_____	_____
Introduce Fruiting Conditions	_____	_____

Blue Thumb   Sean McNamara

Sample Bulk Substrate
Tracking Sheet Pg. 2

First Pins Emerge ⎯⎯⎯⎯⎯ ⎯⎯⎯⎯⎯

First Caps Develop ⎯⎯⎯⎯⎯ ⎯⎯⎯⎯⎯

First Cap Tears its
Veil ⎯⎯⎯⎯⎯ ⎯⎯⎯⎯⎯

Harvest Day ⎯⎯⎯⎯⎯ ⎯⎯⎯⎯⎯

Flood the Tub and
Submerge the Substrate
for 4-6 hours
(optional – for second
flush) ⎯⎯⎯⎯⎯ ⎯⎯⎯⎯⎯

Return to Fruiting
Conditions
(second flush) ⎯⎯⎯⎯⎯ ⎯⎯⎯⎯⎯

First Pins Emerge
(second flush) ⎯⎯⎯⎯⎯ ⎯⎯⎯⎯⎯

First Caps Develop
(second flush) ⎯⎯⎯⎯⎯ ⎯⎯⎯⎯⎯

First Cap Tears its
Veil
(second flush) ⎯⎯⎯⎯⎯ ⎯⎯⎯⎯⎯

Harvest Day
(second flush) ⎯⎯⎯⎯⎯ ⎯⎯⎯⎯⎯

Repeat for third flush and beyond if desired.

Part Eight: Record Keeping

Do You Know Your Schedule?

I cannot provide medical advice in this guide, and some people may misconstrue my recommending a microdosing schedule as doing exactly that. Therefore, I will not recommend a specific schedule.

In this brief chapter, I simply recommend you do your research online and in other books and determine a schedule for taking your microdose on a regular basis.

Some suggest microdosing four days in a row then taking three days off. Others suggest two days on, two days off. Others still, recommend one day on, followed by two days off.

Whatever schedule you choose, write it down. If you already make use of your phone or computer's calendar (and its automatic reminders and alerts), you should add your microdosing schedule to it to help you be consistent.

Recording your schedule will also help you be thoughtfull and deliberate when considering altering your schedule and dose. When you make a change, stick with it long enough to determine whether it's working or if you should make another change.

Regardless of your schedule, you can learn a lot about yourself by keeping a daily microdosing journal. The example on the next two pages offers a framework for what you might record.

Notice near the top of the first page where it asks you to circle whether today is an "On-Day" or "Off-Day." This refers to whether you took a microdose today, or not. This would depend on the schedule you plan for yourself, of course.

I also recommend keeping a dream journal, for both its psychological and spiritual insights.

If you're new to dreamwork or psychic phenomenology, you might read my book *Renegade Mystic*, or try my brief guide *Concise Instructions for Lucid Dreaming and the Out of Body Experience*, both of which include specific instructions for effective dream journaling. They're also available as audiobooks.

Dream journaling is a powerful technique when executed properly.

See www.MindPossible.com for more information, including an online course on the same topic.

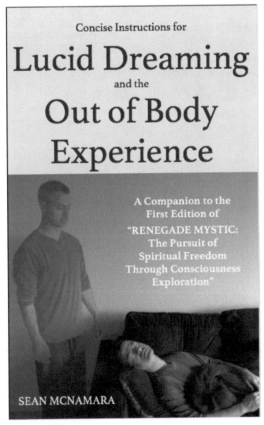

Sample Daily Microdosing Journal
Pg. 1

Dedicate a blank notebook to record the information below. Ideally, you'll do these reflections before bedtime, nightly.

Date:_____ Day of the Week:_____

Circle one:

Today is an On-Day   Today is an Off-Day

Time of day the dosage was taken:_____

Amount and type taken
(for example, 0.075 grams, *dried powder*):

How it was taken (tea, food, capsule, etc.):

General mood *before* taking the dose (if an "On-Day"):

Mood changes *after* taking the dose throughout the remainder of the day:

Sample Daily Microdosing Journal
Pg. 2

Any **positive, healing, productive or pleasant** feelings, sensations, thoughts, or reactions/responses today?

Any strange, uncomfortable, or out of the ordinary feelings, sensations, thoughts, or reactions/responses today?

Does it seem like you need to adjust your dose up or down next time? If so, what should the next dosage measurement be?

* Small changes are recommended, for example going from 0.08 grams to 0.09 grams instead jumping from 0.08 to 0.1. Spend several days or weeks slowly dialing in your ideal dose, remembering to **keep it sub-perceptual**. If you feel anything strange, or slightly "off," that's too much, so back it down.

Common Acronyms and Lingo

brf = brown rice flour

contam = contamination

fae = fresh air exchange

fc = fruiting conditions

ge = gas exchange

knock up = inoculate

lc = liquid culture

lme = light malt extract

noc = inoculate

pc = pressure cooker

pda = potato dextrose agar

PE = Penis Envy

PF = Psilocybe Fanaticus

rh = relative humidity

sab = still air box

sub = substrate

tek = technique

verm = vermiculite

PART NINE:

HARM
REDUCTION

How to Test for Potency

Measuring your dosage before consumption is part of the work of *harm reduction.*

That phrase encompasses supporting your health goals, maintaining personal responsibility and safety, and encouraging lawmakers, politicians, and society-at-large to continue reviewing the scientific data regarding its medical effectiveness in mental health care.

Responsible and effective use includes knowing how potent your psilocybin is. Imagine you're about to finish your current supply of dried mushrooms, and you recently harvested your monotub. Your new crop finished drying and you powdered it and stored it away.

It would be wrong to automatically start using the same dose with the new batch as the old one. 0.08 grams may have kept things "sub-perceptual" (the desired experience, or non-experience, rather). But with the new batch, which may be significantly more potent, 0.08 grams crosses the line, making you feel vaguely "off" or slightly anxious instead of feeling nothing at all.

Therefore, testing a tiny portion of your powdered supply is the smart thing to do. As of this writing, a German company named Miraculix[9] has made an affordable home-test kit available. If you live in the United States, scroll down on their site and click on the "Shipping and Delivery" link to find their U.S. distributor.

I recommend testing each new batch of dried psilocybin before starting a new microdosing regimen.

---

[9] www.miraculix-lab.de/en

This will help you decide whether to alter your dose, and by how much.

Pic 311 shows the home test kit's box.

Pic 312 shows the testing materials and instruction guide. The process is easy.

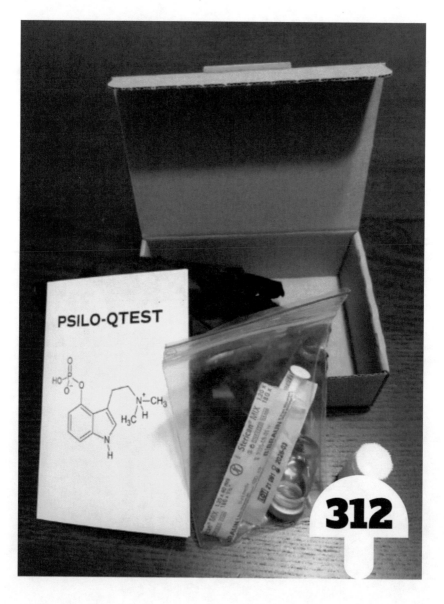

Pic 313 shows the results of the first batch I tested. Notice that the dark fluid indicates the highest potency.

To learn how I made my batch so potent, see the chapter *The Secret to High Potency* in Part Five.

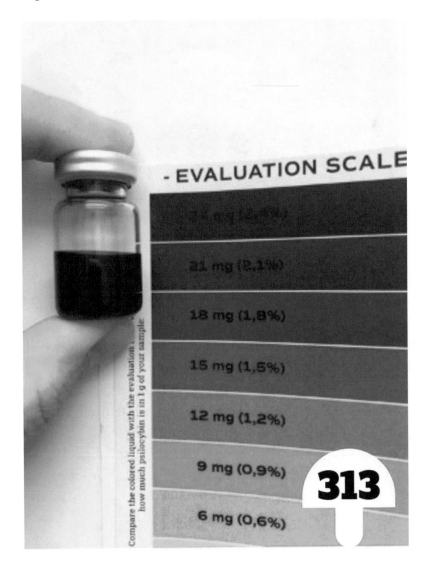

Use an Electronic Food Scale for Dosing

In microdosing, it's important to "dial in" your optimal dose by using an electronic scale. For example, there can be a significant experiential difference between 0.07 grams and 0.1 grams of dried psilocybin, depending on the potency of the powder and the unique sensitivity of the person.

After you find your optimal dose, using a scale <u>every</u> <u>single</u> <u>time</u> helps you maintain accuracy.

If you still need to buy one, it's helpful to use search terms that get you what you need. For example, you might do a search on your favorite retailer's website using the phrase "0.01 food scale."

This way, you'll hopefully be shown scales that measure with that level of specificity.

A scale that only reads down to "0.1 grams," only *tenths* of a gram, isn't helpful for microdosing. You want

Blue Thumb   Sean McNamara

a scale that reads to the "0.<u>01</u> gram," the *hundredths* of a gram level, as in Pic 314 on the previous page.

Again, there can be a significant difference between 0.1 grams and 0.07 grams, and not all scales can measure that difference.

I also recommend weighing your mushrooms for an accurate m<u>a</u>crodose or hero dose. Slapping an unknown weight of dried mushrooms on a peanut butter and jelly sandwich and hoping for the best is irresponsible use.

Beware Bad Microdosing Advice

I recently found a website in which the blogger explicitly recommended 0.35 grams for microdosing. They reasoned that since an "average" hallucinogenic dose is 3.5 grams, 1/10th of that (0.35 grams) would be appropriate for microdosing. The calculation of 1/10th to 1/20th of a hallucinogenic dose to determine a microdose is widely referenced in books and the internet.

Yet, the blogger didn't give any consideration for potency. For example, with the batch I tested on pg. 289 (Pic 313), taking 0.35 grams would be foolish and could leave the microdoser feeling very uncomfortable the rest of the day, possibly crossing the line into **ma̲cro** dosing.

The blogger also didn't consider an individual user's unique sensitivity to psilocybin. Using me as an example, 0.1 grams from the batch from Pic 313 was my upper limit, since my priority as a microdoser was to keep it sub-perceptual.

It's wrong to assume that a person weighing 250 lbs. will experience 0.075 grams differently than a person weighing 140 lbs. Both of their brains weigh close to only 3 lbs., and no matter how long it takes to circulate through the body, the brain is the final destination.

When it comes to psilocybin mushrooms, **there is no such thing as an "average" dose.** And every batch of mixed, powdered mushrooms has a different potency, which you now know how to measure.

Blue Thumb   Sean McNamara

I believe this was a case of a blogger reusing advice they found elsewhere on the internet, without having personally experienced what they wrote about.

Please be careful when taking advice from bloggers who you don't personally know and trust. Many people blog for income by writing about topics they can intersperse with affiliate links. When you click on a shopping link on their site for a vegetable dehydrator, or a sterilized grain bag, vermiculite, or capsule fillers, etc., they earn a small royalty as an affiliate for whoever the retailer is.

Professional bloggers write about hot topics so they can get more clicks. So, although they can't be experts at everything, that doesn't stop them from writing about…well, just about everything.

That type of blogging poses a risk to unsuspecting and uneducated readers. It also does nothing to support our efforts to make political, legal, and social inroads for public access to psilocybin by modeling responsible use.

Society and its lawmakers trust us to responsibly dose our daily servings of alcohol, nicotine, caffeine, sugar, marijuana, pain pills, online poker, food supplements, and social media.

Let's show them we're perfectly capable of dosing our psilocybin mushrooms for wellness without a doctor's prescription, or anybody else's permission.

Better than Ayahuasca and Peyote

This chapter's title may raise a few eyebrows at first glance. But keep in mind this chapter is placed in the section on harm reduction. Instead of reducing harm to oneself, this chapter discusses reducing harm to others.

North and south of the U.S.-Mexican border, indigenous cultures who have used peyote for traditional practices for many generations are now facing an extreme shortage of the extremely slow growing cactus.

In the 2020 paper *Peyote Crisis Confronting Modern Indigenous Peoples: The Declining Peyote Population and a Demand for Conservation*,[10] we learn that farming, mining, and modern infrastructure are destroying the fragile environment required for peyote to thrive.

And the other culprit is *psychedelic tourism.* Non-indigenous people hire guides to help them locate the cacti, and the tourists take as much as they can without considering the cultural needs of the indigenous people who still maintain an honorable relationship with the cactus. The 2022 docuseries, *How to Change Your Mind*[11] touches on this. Or you can read the book it's based on, with the same title.

---

[10] Muneta, J. (December 23, 2020). *Peyote Crisis Confronting Modern Indigenous Peoples: The Declining Peyote Population and a Demand for Conservation.* American Indian Law Journal. Volume 9, Issue 1.

[11] Pollan, M., Gibney, A. (2022). *How to Change Your Mind.* Distributed by Netflix. https://michaelpollan.com/books/how-to-change-your-mind/

Blue Thumb   Sean McNamara

Non-indigenous people are also wreaking havoc in the Amazon through psychedelic tourism. The economic force of the dollar is driving the creation of healing centers through the collaboration (or coercion?) between entrepreneurs and shamans.

Some of the shamans are authentic and earnest. Others may have questionable credentials and even less honorable intentions.

Worse, authentic shamans are being forced out of their own villages by aggressive, competitive market forces. To witness an example of this, watch the documentary *The Last Shaman*.[12] It should break your heart.

The point is that you can reduce the harm being done to entire cultures right now if you **abstain from psychedelic tourism.**

If a person believes they deserve to fly someplace exotic to experience healing at the cost of destroying ecosystems and indigenous people's access to their own medicine, I hope they will think twice.

Sometimes, healing begins with humility. And humility increases empathy. Then compassion.

If you really want to travel, consider Jamaica, the Bahamas, Brazil, or Portugal.[13]

Why go anywhere else when you can easily grow psilocybin inside a box in your living room without hurting other people or our fragile planet?

That's why psilocybin is better than peyote and ayahuasca.

---

[12] Degan, R. (2016). *The Last Shaman*. Distributed by Netflix. https://www.thelastshaman.com/

[13] Check their national laws for changes before booking your flights.

About the Author

Sean McNamara lives in Denver, Colorado. He is a therapist, teacher, author, consciousness explorer, and husband. He has a master's degree in clinical mental health counseling and a bachelor's degree in computer science. He enjoys walks in nature, road trips, paddleboarding, and exploring the subtle nature of consciousness.

To learn more about him, visit either of his sites:

www.LifeTending.net   www.MindPossible.com

Made in the USA
Columbia, SC
16 January 2024

30494990R00170